Table of Contents

M&T CHIMNEY and ROOFING

Introduction

If you are thinking about buying a wood-heating appliance or already heat your home with wood, you may be one of 3 million Canadian households that appreciate the ambience and warmth of wood heat. Wood heating has a long history in Canada and, with new available technologies, more households are returning to wood for renewable energy.

Wood-heating technologies have changed a lot in the past decade. Today's advanced combustion systems burn more cleanly and efficiently than ever.

If you are shopping for a wood-heating appliance or are planning to replace or upgrade your current unit, consider only a highly efficient combustion appliance. You can identify these advanced systems by looking for proof of certification to the performance standards set by both CSA International, formerly the Canadian Standards Association, ("CSA B415.1 Performance Testing of Solid-Fuel-Burning Heating Appliances") and the U.S. Environmental Protection Agency (EPA 1990). Certified systems will give you a cleaner, more efficient burn.

If you are already enjoying the benefits of wood heat in your home, use this guide to help you make informed decisions on such matters as the following:

- consulting wood-heating professionals;
- how to maintain your system for safety and peak efficiency;
- how to purchase and store your fuel wood;
- how to use fire management techniques for cleaner, virtually smokeless fires; and
- many other useful tips.

This guide is part of a series of buyer's guides on renewable energy systems for residential use. More documents on residential wood heating include these titles:

- *All About Wood Fireplaces*
- *An Introduction to Home Heating With Wood*
- *Buying a High-Efficiency Wood-Burning Appliance*
- *Getting the Most Out of Your Wood Stove*

For electronic versions of these guides, visit the Web site at http://www.nrcan.gc.ca/es/erb/reed/public_e.htm. You can also order copies free of charge by calling 1 800 387-2000 toll-free.

1 Safety Tips – Burn It Smart!

Enjoy the benefits of your wood fire in comfort just by taking a few simple precautions. Otherwise, in the blink of an eye, those warm friendly flames in your fireplace or wood stove could turn into a devastating fire. You can easily prevent dangerous situations such as chimney fires by taking the proper safety measures.

Here are some good tips on ways to burn cleaner wood fires.

Safety

Keep creosote at bay

Creosote, a crusty deposit left behind by the smoke that drifts up your chimney, can ignite into a dangerous fire when it builds up. To reduce it:

✔ Burn only clean, well-seasoned wood that has been split and dried properly. Dry wood lights faster, burns better and produces less smoke than "green" wood – a major culprit in creosote buildup.

✔ Think twice before you chop up that old coffee table and toss it into your wood stove. Burning garbage, plastic, particleboard, plywood, salted driftwood or any other painted or treated wood releases a toxic cloud of chemicals and can build up creosote.

Don't let a small spark ignite a big blaze

✔ The best way to start your fire is with newspaper and dry kindling. Never try to get a blaze roaring with gasoline, kerosene or charcoal starter – you will get more firepower than you bargained for.

✔ Remove ashes from your stove or fireplace regularly and store them in a covered metal container in a safe area away from the side of your house. The sparks in hot ashes can easily start fires.

✔ Keep all household items – drapes, furniture, newspaper and books – away from the heat and the stray sparks of your woodstove or fireplace.

✔ Protect floors from sparks with a properly fitted screen around your fireplace. A decorative screen does not provide protection.

Detection devices save lives

✔ Install carbon monoxide detectors and smoke alarms, as required by the *National Fire Code of Canada*, and keep a fire extinguisher nearby. You should never smell smoke in your house. If you do, it usually means your wood stove or fireplace system isn't venting properly – perhaps the chimney is blocked, a damper is faulty or the fireplace is competing with your range hood. Not only are these fire hazards, but they could also lead to deadly carbon monoxide poisoning.

A hot new stove

✔ If you are using an open fireplace or your wood stove is past its prime, you might consider buying a new model with improved safety and efficiency features. The best choice is a **high-efficiency** stove or fireplace approved for safety by the Underwriters' Laboratories of Canada (ULC) or another testing body, and certified as low-emission by the U.S. Environmental Protection Agency (EPA).

Go to the professionals

✔ Any new stove or fireplace should be professionally installed. Make sure your existing unit is inspected and cleaned at least once a year by a technician certified under the Wood Energy Technical Training (WETT) program or, in Quebec, the Association des professionnels du chauffage.

Healthier Wood Heat

The hottest pollution preventer

✔ The best way to reduce wood smoke is by using a high-efficiency wood stove or fireplace, certified low-emission by the EPA. Used properly, these products cut emissions by up to 90 percent, and you will see virtually no smoke coming from your chimney.

✔ More efficient than conventional models, high-efficiency products use up to one third less wood – meaning less smoke, less work and hearty cost savings.

Burn small and burn smart

✔ Keep the fire hot and small. Feed it regularly with split wood and never let it smoulder. A smouldering fire creates more smoke.

✔ Don't overload your stove or fireplace. Air should move around inside for a cleaner burn.

Where there's smoke... there's pollution

✔ Burn dry, well-seasoned wood that has been split properly. Green wood produces unhealthy smoke because it is too wet.

✔ Burning garbage, plastic, particleboard, plywood or any other painted or treated wood releases a toxic cloud of chemicals – don't toss these items into your fire.

Be energy efficient

✔ Make sure your home is energy efficient by insulating walls, caulking windows and repairing weatherstripping around the doors. Don't let your heat slip through the cracks!

Local Air Quality Advisory

✔ Under certain weather conditions, you will notice that the smoke is slow to thin out and hangs in the air for longer than usual. Sometimes Canadian municipalities will issue local air quality advisories in which people are asked not to burn wood during this time. It's important to respect these advisories.

> *Scientific research and the co-operative efforts of governments and industry make wood burning safer, cleaner, more convenient and more efficient than ever.*

Wood was Canada's original heating fuel. Wood burning continues to be an effective and economical way to heat your home – as a primary heating source or as a secondary heating source to complement conventional oil or gas furnaces, or electric baseboards.

Advances in Wood Burning

Major advances in the 1990s have made wood burning cleaner and more effective, efficient and convenient than ever. The following are some of these advances:

- combustion designs that can burn more of the wood – and burn it more cleanly and at higher efficiencies;

- performance standards (CSA B415.1 and EPA 1990) that identify newer, cleaner-burning units;

- technology that provides more efficient heating while allowing you to view the flame from behind a special ceramic glass door that will stay clear for long periods;

- pellet stoves that use compressed wood and other biomass wastes, capable of providing at least 24 hours of unattended, automated heating;

- standards that provide clear guidelines for safe installation; and

- professional training programs for installers and inspectors to ensure that you get dependable advice and service.

As recently as the mid-1970s, basement wood furnaces or simple box stoves burned most of the wood in homes. Then came the evolution to airtight stoves, which were more efficient but created more air pollution. Pressured by environmental observers over the issue of smoke pollution, stove designers began to develop cleaner-burning products. By the early 1990s, Canadian manufacturers led the way, and new products reached the market.

Today, the efficiency of wood-heating systems has improved significantly. Most of the new wood-heating appliances are attractive stoves and fireplaces designed for the main living areas of a home. They use advanced technology and are cleaner-burning. Such appliances, properly installed in the right place, can provide primary or secondary heat for your home – while offering the beauty of a visible fire.

Our houses have also become more energy efficient, with more insulation, more effective air barriers, and sealed doors and windows. These changes make houses easier to heat. But they also mean that wood-burning systems must be better designed and sized and their installation carefully planned so that they function properly within a tightly sealed house.

The Keys to Safe and Successful Wood Burning

The keys to safe and successful wood burning are good planning, carefully selecting a high-efficiency appliance, installing and properly operating the appliance and practising clean-burning habits. This guide is intended to help you plan and use your wood-burning system in the safest, cleanest and most effective way.

3 Wood Burning and **the Environment**

> *Wood is a renewable energy resource. And because trees recycle carbon dioxide, wood burning doesn't contribute to the problem of climate change. As well, advanced combustion technologies mean more heat and less smoke from the wood you burn.*

Any fuel you choose to heat your home will affect the environment. When wood is not burned properly, it can have negative impacts on both outdoor and indoor air quality. Smouldering, smoky fires that produce a plume of blue-grey smoke from the chimney are the main cause of air pollution related to wood burning. You can reduce the amount of smoke from wood heating in many ways.

- If possible, upgrade to a new, cleaner-burning stove or fireplace. Cleaner-burning appliances are certified to CSA International's CSA B415.1 smoke emissions standard or to U.S. Environmental Protection Agency rules. These appliances reduce smoke emissions by as much as 90 percent compared with conventional wood stoves, fireplaces and furnaces. Ask your hearth products retailer for details.

- Select an appliance that is the right size for your home's heating needs, and place it in the main living area to make the best use of the heat it produces.

- Use a modern chimney matched to your appliance.

- Avoid smouldering fires by using the clean-burn techniques covered in Chapter 10, "Preventing Smoke, Smells and Cold Hearths." Burning wood cleanly reduces up to half the amount of smoke produced.

- Use well-seasoned, dry, clean firewood that is split to the right size for your appliance.

- Make your house more energy efficient so that you use less fuel to heat it. Using less fuel wood means less environmental impact and less work on your part.

Wood Burning, Climate Change and the Carbon Cycle

Nearly every day, we read news reports about the need to reduce emissions of greenhouse gases (GHGs) to prevent climate change and related problems. The main source of GHGs is the burning of oil, gas and coal to produce the energy we use. These fuels are called fossil fuels because they are taken from deep beneath the earth's surface, where they have been formed over millions of years. When fossil fuels are burned, GHGs are released. The main GHG is carbon dioxide (CO_2). Increased concentrations of these gases in the atmosphere trap the sun's heat close to the earth and cause the average global temperature to rise.

Wood, however, differs from fossil fuels such as oil and gas because it is carbon neutral. The term "renewable" refers to the fact that trees recycle CO_2. As a tree grows, it uses CO_2 from the air as a source of carbon to build its structure. This carbon makes up about half of the weight of wood. When wood is burned, it decomposes rapidly, and CO_2 is released into the atmosphere again. A similar amount of CO_2 would be slowly released if the tree died and was left to rot on the forest floor. As a result, wood heating doesn't contribute to the problem of climate change the way fossil fuel use does. But wood fuel is truly renewable only if it is produced by using sustainable forestry practices. Canada's forests can be a perpetual source of fuel – as long as they are cared for and managed properly.

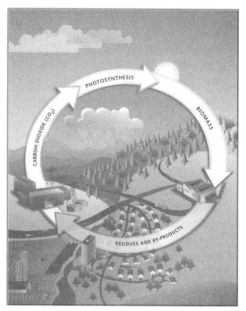

▲ *The Carbon Cycle*

In the mid-1980s, researchers and appliance designers began to develop new technologies to significantly reduce the amount of smoke and other pollutants that wood-burning appliances produce. Complete combustion needs three simultaneous conditions: high temperature, enough oxygen (air) and time for the combustion gases to burn before being cooled.

Today, these highly efficient technologies come in three categories: advanced combustion, catalytic, and densified pellet systems.

Advanced Combustion Systems

Highly efficient combustion systems create the conditions needed to burn the smoke before it leaves the appliance. The technology has the following characteristics:

- firebox insulation to keep temperatures high;

- primary combustion air that is preheated so that it doesn't cool the fire;

- preheated secondary air that is fed to the fire through sets of small holes in the gas-burning zone, above and behind the fuel bed; and

- internal baffles that give the gases a long and hot enough route so that they can burn completely.

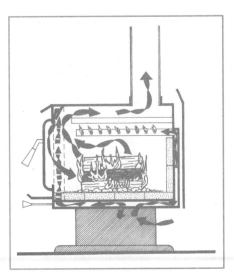

▲ *Advanced combustion system*

When wood in a combustion stove or fireplace is burning well, you may see nearly transparent flames swirling above the wood in addition to the normal flames coming from the wood.

Canadian manufacturers have an international reputation as designers of some of the most effective wood-burning appliances in the world. Ask your hearth products retailer to point these appliances out.

Catalytic Stoves

Catalytic stoves rely on a catalyst to help burn smoke before it leaves the appliance. The catalyst in a wood-burning appliance is a coated ceramic honeycomb-shaped device through which the exhaust gas is routed. The catalytic coating lowers the ignition temperature of the combustion gases as they pass through it. This allows catalytic appliances to burn cleanly at low heat output settings. The performance of the catalyst deteriorates over time and emissions rise accordingly, so you need to replace the catalyst now and then.

Because the catalyst restricts gas flow through the appliance, catalytic stoves always include a bypass damper into the flue. The damper is opened when fuel is loaded and is closed when you get a hot fire. This forces the gases through the catalyst for an extended, cleaner burn. The restriction of gas flow can also cause draft problems.

Densified Pellet Systems

Densified pellet systems burn fuel made from dried ground wood or other biomass waste compressed into small cylinders about 6 mm (1/4 in.) in diameter and 25 mm (1 in.) long. The pressure and heat created during their production binds the pellets together with the lignin in the wood without using additives.

Pellet burners include a hopper to hold 20–60 kg of fuel and a screw auger to automatically move the pellets from the hopper into the combustion chamber. Pellets burn cleanly because they are fed to the chamber at a controlled rate and are matched with the right amount of combustion air. If they are properly adjusted, pellet-burning stoves can operate at lower emissions levels than natural firewood appliances.

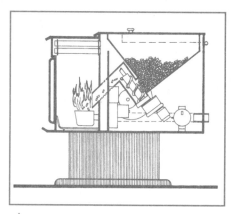

▲ *Densified pellet system*

Since pellet stoves have three or even four motors, they can use a lot of electricity. If possible, try to get a pellet stove that uses efficient electric motors. DC motors use the least amount of energy – only 40–120 watts in total. To ensure that your pellet stove is efficient and clean-burning, buy one that has been tested to CSA B415.1 or EPA 1990 standards.

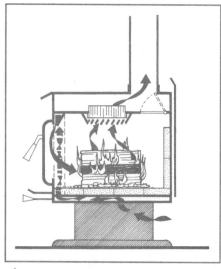

▲ *Catalytic stove*

5 Heating Options

Most Canadian homes are heated by a central system, either a furnace or boiler (usually located in the basement). The heat is distributed around the house through ducts (hot air) or in pipes (hot water). Space heaters tend to heat the area in which they are located.

You have many options for heating your home with wood. These options, discussed below, include space heaters such as wood stoves and fireplaces, as well as central heating systems.

SPACE HEATERS

Most wood-burning appliances function primarily as space heaters. A space heater is intended to heat a space directly, unlike a central heating furnace or boiler, which supplies heat to the house through a system of ducts or pipes. In the past, when houses were poorly insulated and drafty, a space heater could be expected only to heat the room it was installed in and possibly an adjacent space. Modern houses conserve energy more effectively and need less heat to stay warm. Now a single space heater can provide most of the heat for a well-insulated, average-sized home.

Like any effective heating system, installing a space heater takes careful planning. If you intend to supply most of your home's heating needs with a space heater, consider these two important factors:

1) The heater should be located where household members spend most of their time.

2) The heat must be able to circulate to other parts of the house.

These conditions aren't difficult to meet, but they do need to be planned.

Space heaters come in several different forms. They include wood stoves, cookstoves, pellet stoves, conventional fireplaces, high-efficiency fireplaces, fireplace inserts and masonry heaters.

Wood Stoves

The wood stove is the most common wood-heating appliance. It can be safely located almost anywhere as long as there is enough space and a chimney can be properly routed. The ideal place for the space heater is in the centre of the main-floor living area of the house, with the flue pipe running straight up from the stove flue collar into the chimney. This type of installation provides the best performance and requires the least maintenance. However, keep in mind that all wood-heating appliances need regular upkeep for safety, efficiency and cleanliness. Wood stoves come in a wide range of sizes and designs.

Heat Output

Wood stoves range from very small units, designed to heat only a small area, to large stoves that can heat large houses. However, large-output stoves work well only if your house has an open-plan design, where the heat can readily circulate to other areas.

Selecting a stove with the correct heat output range can be tricky because the stove's appearance doesn't always reflect its performance. If the stove's output is too large for the space to be heated, it will be turned down low much of the time, producing a smoky fire. An undersized stove, meanwhile, may deteriorate because of constant over-firing. What is the best way to find a stove that is sized for your needs? Get advice from an experienced wood stove retailer. Since these retailers know the performance of each of their stoves, they can help you choose one that has the right output for the space you want to heat.

Design

The exterior designs of wood stoves owe more to aesthetics and personal preference than to performance. For example, there are no clear differences in performance between cast iron and plate steel constructions or between painted and enamelled finishes. The real difference is the technology inside the conventional wood stove as opposed to the technology in the high-efficiency wood stove.

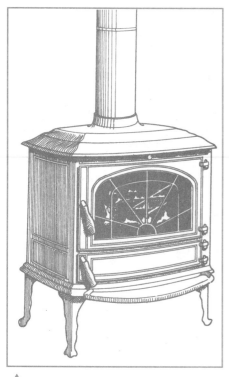

▲ CAST-IRON WOOD STOVES – Cast-iron wood stoves deliver much of their heat to the room by direct radiation. Rear heat shields, however, are often used to reduce installation clearances. These shields create convection air flow.

Means of Heat Transfer

Various stove designs heat the room in different ways. Depending on its design, a wood stove may deliver most of its heat by direct radiation, by the convection flow of warmed air, or both.

Radiation is the direct transfer of heat from the hot stove surfaces to walls, furniture and people that are in direct line of sight from the stove. Radiant energy will make you feel warm, even though the air around you is cool. The ceramic glass in the new wood stoves has special properties that allow direct radiation from the flame to pass through it. So you get heat through the glass, as well as from the hot metal surfaces of the stove.

Convection is the transfer of heat through the motion of air. In wood stoves that deliver heat by convection, the body of the stove is surrounded by an outer casing, usually made of sheet metal. Heat from the stove creates a current of air in the space between the body and the outer casing. This way, much of the heat from the stove is delivered to the room as warmed air, rather than direct radiation. The outer surfaces of convection stoves (and the shielded portions of other stoves) don't get as hot as unshielded surfaces.

When you shop for a stove, you will notice that most new wood stoves deliver heat to a room by a **combination of direct radiation and convection**. The sides and rear of many stoves are shielded so that they can be installed close to walls, and these shields create convection flow of warm air. The fronts of all stoves, either with glass panels or solid metal doors, deliver heat directly to the room.

Cookstoves

▲ Generations of rural Canadians used wood-burning cookstoves not only for preparing meals and heating water, but also for heating their homes.

You may find that a cookstove is a desirable addition to your rural home. However, cookstoves aren't designed for use as stand-alone home-heating devices. And even though their manufacturers have been developing efficient, clean-burning products, smoky fires can still be a problem.

Pellet Stoves

Stoves that burn pellet fuels – made from wood, corn or other biomass wastes – have been widely available in Canada for several years. Pellet stoves have some advantages over wood stoves that burn firewood:

- The automatic operation is convenient.

- One hopper-load of fuel can last 24 hours or more.

- The fuel is supplied in compact bags that store neatly.

- Most can use a special vent that costs less than wood-stove chimneys.

- They can offer low emissions and high efficiency.

Balancing these advantages are some limitations that you should consider:

- Pellet stoves tend to cost more.

- Pellet fuel is more expensive than firewood in many areas.

- Most pellet stoves need electricity to drive auger motors and fans.

- Flames produced by pellet stoves don't look as natural as wood fires, although this feature has improved.

At the same time, pellet stoves usually have three motorized systems that require electricity.

1) a fuel feed auger to move the fuel from the storage hopper to the combustion chamber;

2) an exhaust fan to move the exhaust gases through the appliance and into the venting system while drawing in combustion air; and

3) a circulating fan to force air through the heat exchanger and into the room.

A few pellet stoves can operate during electrical power failures by using batteries to operate the motors.

Although stoves are the most common pellet-burning appliances, you may also find fireplaces and central heating furnaces that burn pellet fuel in your area. Depending on your circumstances, a pellet-burning appliance could be a very practical heating option.

▲ *Pellet stoves have a more complex interior than wood stoves. A motorized auger feeds the pellets to the combustion chamber, and a fan forces the exhaust into the venting system. An air circulation fan is also standard equipment on pellet stoves. On the other hand, they are easier to use and you can control the temperature.*

Conventional Fireplaces

Conventional fireplaces have a long history in Canadian home heating. They are built from masonry materials such as brick, block and stone. More recently, factory-built models are constructed mainly of steel. These fireplaces were designed for, and are only useful for, your enjoyment of the fire.

Conventional wood-burning fireplaces don't heat a home effectively. Tests show that they can cause major heat loss by drawing heated air out of the house while delivering little heat to the room. This problem can actually make the house feel drafty while the fireplace is operating and can result in a near- or below-zero efficiency when it is cold outside. Conventional fireplaces perform poorly because they don't have the characteristics needed to convert the fuel to useful heat – such as tight-fitting casketed doors, well-designed combustion chambers and an adequate heat exchanger.

Not only are conventional fireplaces inefficient and drafty, they can create two other problems. First, their simple fireboxes don't burn the wood completely, so air pollution can be high. Second, their large air consumption, poor combustion and widely varying draft make them more likely than other types of wood-burning systems to spill smoke into the room. These days, Canadians are more concerned about indoor air pollution than ever. If you share that concern, avoid using a conventional fireplace in your home.

If you already have a conventional fireplace and would like to upgrade it, be a little sceptical about the claims made for many fireplace products. While manufacturers advertise many options that claim to improve the performance of a conventional fireplace, in reality most do little to increase efficiency or decrease pollutants.

For example, to reduce the cold draft, you could install tempered-glass doors on the fireplace. The doors won't improve energy efficiency, but they may reduce the leakage of air when you aren't using the fireplace.

Note, too, that the tempered glass used in most fireplace doors (unlike the ceramic glass used for new wood stoves) blocks much of the radiant heat coming from the fire.

You may think that installing a tubular grate or special firebox liner will improve the fireplace's heating efficiency. However, this option isn't recommended because it makes only a minor improvement. And continuous use of the fireplace could dangerously overheat the surrounding area.

Installing an outside combustion air duct to the firebox is unlikely to improve performance and can become a fire hazard under certain wind conditions. Air from the outdoors can reverse flow direction, sending hot exhaust gases through the duct.

If you use your open-pit fireplace only occasionally to view a fire, artificial fire logs made of wax and sawdust are a good alternative to natural firewood. Efficiency won't be high, but pollutants will be reduced.

However, if you want to use your fireplace on a regular basis and want better all-round performance, your best option is to upgrade it with an advanced combustion fireplace insert or hearth-mount stove. By upgrading your system, you will notice more heat, much fewer pollutants and fewer cold drafts while enjoying your fireplace. Moreover, you will still be able to view an attractive fire.

▲ *Conventional open-pit fireplace*

High-Efficiency Fireplaces

If you are looking for a new fireplace installation, you can now combine the beauty of a fireplace with the heating power of a wood stove by selecting one of the new breeds of advanced factory-built fireplaces. Advanced combustion, high-efficiency fireplaces are becoming as effective for space heating as the new, advanced wood stoves. They use the same internal combustion features to reduce smoke emissions and boost efficiency.

The firebox and heat exchanger of these fireplaces are surrounded by an insulated sheet-metal casing. This means they can be installed within a combustible construction without overheating it. A lumber or steel-stud frame is constructed and sheathed with drywall or other materials to enclose the sides and rear of the fireplace. The enclosure can then be decorated with tile, brick or stone slices and a mantel to create either a traditional- or modern-style fireplace. In most cases, the fireplace and its decorative facing materials can be installed without a foundation or floor reinforcement.

These fireplaces provide heat to the room by drawing air through a grille (below the firebox) into the circulation chamber (between the firebox and casing), where it is heated. This heated air is directed back into the room either through another grille above the fireplace opening or through one or more ducts.

▲ *Factory-built fireplaces feature advanced combustion systems, tight-fitting ceramic glass doors and heat exchangers. Some have optional duct kits to distribute warm air to other parts of the home.*

Some advanced fireplaces are approved for additional duct routing to any part of the house.

These new fireplaces, approved to CSA International or EPA performance standards, can meet both heating and aesthetic objectives. Their only real drawback is the complex installation, which you should leave to trained professionals.

Fireplace Inserts

A fireplace insert is like a wood stove, but designed to be installed within the firebox of an existing masonry fireplace. Inserts are used to convert masonry fireplaces into more effective heating systems. An insert consists of a firebox surrounded by an insulated convection shell. Air flows through the shell to be warmed before being returned to the room. The outer shell ensures that most of the heat is delivered to the room instead of being trapped behind the insert in the masonry structure.

▲ *You can retrofit an existing masonry fireplace with an insert to improve its efficiency and reduce the amount of air exhausted from the house.*

A decorative faceplate covers the space between the insert body and the fireplace opening.

Fireplace inserts used to have a reputation for being unsafe, inefficient and expensive to maintain because the exhaust wasn't properly vented to the outdoors. Many older installations allowed the exhaust gas to exit the insert flue collar and find its way up the chimney. In an attempt to correct this problem, homeowners sometimes used a short length of stainless steel liner to connect the flue collar to the base of the fireplace chimney. However, experience has shown that, even with a direct chimney connection, inserts didn't work properly. Aside from poor combustion, many inserts did a poor job of transferring heat from one room to another. They were also hard to clean and generated a high level of creosote. Creosote is an oily liquid with a penetrating odour, obtained by distilling wood tar. When your chimney is caked with creosote, your risk for chimney fires increases significantly.

Municipal installation codes now require that a properly sized, stainless-steel chimney liner be installed from the insert flue collar to the top of the chimney. The result is better performance and a safer system.

The liner reduces the flue size to match the insert. It also isolates the exhaust gas from the masonry structure of the fireplace and its chimney. **Your new insert should be certified for low emissions so that you get the full benefits of the advanced technologies.** This design evolution and technology have increased performance to the extent that today's best fireplace inserts, with ceramic glass doors and insulated outer casing, are nearly as efficient as freestanding wood stoves.

Perhaps you already have an insert installed in a masonry fireplace. Adding a stainless-steel chimney liner would greatly improve performance and safety.

A few special inserts can be installed in factory-built fireplaces. If you are considering using an insert to improve the performance of your conventional factory-built fireplace, be sure that it is certified for this use.

Hearth-Mount Stoves

A **hearth-mount stove** is an alternative to a fireplace insert. A hearth mount is a wood stove installed in front of a fireplace. Or, if you have a large fireplace, it can be mounted partially inside its firebox and vented through the fireplace chimney. Like inserts, hearth mounts must be vented through a liner that is continuous from the flue collar to the top of the chimney. It is usually more efficient than an

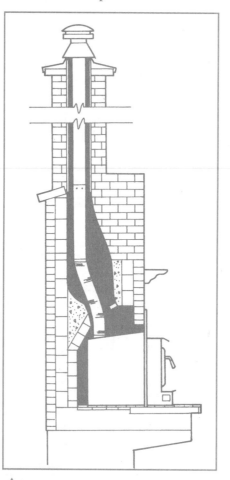

▲ *Municipal installation codes now require that a properly sized, stainless-steel chimney liner be installed from the insert flue collar to the top of the chimney. The result is better performance and a safer system*

insert, as heat from the casing comes directly into the room. You can use only certain wood stoves as hearth mounts. The certification label and installation instructions indicate if the unit can be vented through a fireplace.

High-Thermal-Mass Masonry Heaters

High-thermal-mass masonry heaters operate on a different principle from high-efficiency, factory-built fireplaces. Masonry heaters take advantage of tonnes of mass – in the form of bricks or stone – to absorb and later release the heat from the fire.

These heaters also have a completely different interior from conventional masonry fireplaces. The core of the heater, consisting of the firebox and heat exchange channels, is built from high-temperature firebrick and/or precast masonry components. To complete the fireplace, the core is then surrounded by brick, tile or stone.

With a masonry heater, you need only one or two hot fires each day to provide all of the heat that your home needs. The wood is burned quickly and the fire is allowed to go out. But the heat stored in the masonry structure continues to radiate warmth for many hours thereafter.

The Masonry Heater Association of North America has developed guidelines for the efficient design and installation of these heaters. Be sure that your unit meets these requirements. Since a masonry heater represents a considerable investment, consult a professional installer experienced in its design, construction and installation.

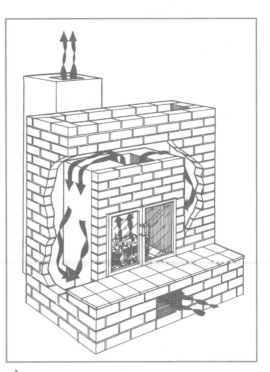

▲ Unlike conventional fireplaces, masonry heaters burn more cleanly and are a more efficient source of heat. The heat from the fire is transferred to the mass of the masonry before being slowly released to the room. Masonry heaters aren't rated for emissions, but you can achieve equivalent performance by following guidelines from the Masonry Heater Association of North America.

CENTRAL HEATING

A central heating system uses a network of air ducts or water pipes to distribute heat to all areas of the house. For example, furnaces heat air that is then forced through ducts with a fan. Boilers heat water that is forced through pipes with a pump. Most houses in Canada have central heating systems that use oil, gas or electricity as energy sources.

Central heating with wood-fired furnaces and boilers is less common than it used to be. Houses are now more energy efficient and easier to heat with wood-burning space heaters and advanced fireplaces, which also offer the aesthetics of fire viewing. As well, furnace and boiler-combustion technology has lagged behind the advances in wood stoves. Presently, no commercial units come close to achieving the low emission levels – or the higher efficiencies – of advanced wood stoves.

However, central heating with a wood-fired furnace may still be an option under the following conditions:

- the house is old, large and not energy efficient;

- the house has many small rooms with no large open areas;

- there is no suitable place to install a fireplace or wood stove;

- fire viewing is a low priority;

- you have ready access to large amounts of low-cost wood fuel; or

- you clean your furnace and venting system frequently.

Add-On Wood Furnace Installation

Wood furnaces and boilers can be installed to work automatically with appliances that use other fuels, such as oil, natural gas and electricity. Combination furnaces (such as wood-oil or wood-electric) have two energy sources in a single packaged unit. Add-on furnaces and boilers can be installed beside existing furnaces and boilers that use other fuels. In general, wood-burning furnaces must have greater clearances from combustible surfaces (e.g. ceiling joists, frame walls) than oil, gas or electric furnaces. All units must be safety tested and certified.

Because wood furnaces lack advanced combustion features, they produce more smoke and deposit more creosote in their chimneys. If you choose a wood-burning central furnace, be prepared to service the chimney, flue pipes and furnace heat exchanger regularly during the winter.

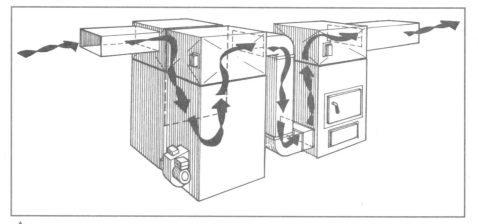

▲ *The add-on is placed beside the existing furnace, and special ducts are installed to connect the two units. The air passes through the original furnace, then through the add-on and into the ducts to be distributed throughout the house. Note that only an experienced professional should install an add-on.*

Outdoor Boiler

An outdoor boiler is contained in a small structure that looks like a garden shed. Heated water from the boiler is pumped through a pipe underground to the house. Here it either passes through a heat exchanger, releasing its heat to a forced air stream, or is distributed to various areas supplying heat to baseboard or wall registers or through floor-heating coils. The water is then sent back to the boiler through a second underground pipe to be reheated.

Uncertified outdoor boilers have become more popular in the past decade. These boilers confine the mess of chips and bark from wood storage and handling to the outdoors. You can use the boiler to heat tap water, as well as your home. Another advantage is that you can use one of these units to heat more than one building.

Some outdoor boilers make so much smoke and air pollution that many neighbours complain. Numerous rural municipalities in Canada have either considered banning them or are proceeding to do so.

There are many problems with outdoor boilers that make them controversial and, in many cases, undesirable. Most outdoor boilers create a lot of smoke during operation for the following reasons:

- they lack internal features that promote complete combustion of the wood;

- the relatively cool boiler surfaces quench the flames;

- the units are inefficient;

- the units selected are often too large for the heat load, which results in smouldering;

- their large fireboxes encourage owners to use large pieces of unsplit, unseasoned firewood that burn inefficiently;

- few municipalities authorize permits for their installation;

- their on/off operating cycle means excessive combustion, which creates high creosote pollution during the off cycle; and

- they smoulder for long periods when used to produce domestic hot water during the summer, producing high levels of smoke emissions.

You might consider buying some accessories to enhance your wood-heating system. Some of the options discussed below can make wood burning more pleasant and convenient, while others can create problems.

Tool Set

There are standard sets of tools for managing a wood fire to heat your home. You will use these tools several times a day during periods of regular heating, so get a set that is more practical than decorative. Tool sets for wood-heating appliances are different from the more decorative sets used with conventional fireplaces. Stove tool sets have shorter handles and have an ash rake instead of a poker. Any retailer that specializes in hearth accessories can help you identify which sets are best suited for your appliance.

Ash Container

You will want to set an effective routine for dealing with ashes. Following are three ways to avoid creating dust as you remove the ashes:

- if your stove has an ash pan, empty it regularly (don't let it over-fill) and transfer the ashes from the pan to a larger, covered **metal** bucket outdoors (never indoors);

- use an accessory ash scoop with a sliding lid to reduce the dust in your home; and

- if you use a shovel and bucket, remove ashes from the stove slowly and never drop ashes from the shovel into the bucket. Warm splattered ashes are a fire hazard.

Double-bottom ash buckets and ash scoops are available from wood-heating retailers.

Fire Screen

For safety and performance reasons, you must operate most wood stoves with their doors closed. However, a few stove models are safety certified for use with their doors open and a special fire screen in place. The screen is offered as an option with these models. Be aware that stoves operating this way are less efficient and produce more smoke emissions than they would with their doors closed. At any rate, never use a fire screen that isn't specifically certified for use with your stove. Screens used only for decoration are no substitute for a safely closed stove door.

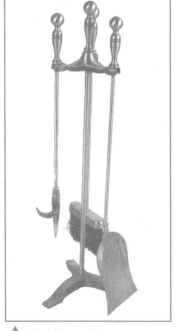

▲ *Fireplace tool set*

▲ *Ash bucket*

Domestic Hot-Water Coil or Tank

Heating household tap water with a wood stove may seem like an attractive idea, but it is rarely feasible because such systems are complicated and expensive. Poorly designed systems can also be hazardous. Without proper design and pressure-relief devices, steam can become trapped and cause a violent explosion. The hot-water coil or tank must be safety certified for use with your stove. If you decide to have a hot-water system installed, get advice from an experienced stove retailer. Also, make sure that the manufacturer's instructions for installing it are followed exactly. Such coils may also degrade the performance of a clean-burning, advanced combustion appliance, resulting in high emissions and creosote.

Humidifier

Does the air in your house tend to be dry in winter? Do you notice too much static electricity and have a dry nose and mouth? If so, consider adding humidity to your air. The simplest form of humidifier is a cast-iron pot of water left to evaporate on the stove. Decorative cast-iron humidifiers designed for this purpose are available from wood heat retailers. However, you **don't** need humidification if you see any sign of condensation on windows during cold weather. Also, in new, energy-tight houses, problems can arise from too much moisture indoors. Experiment to find the best moisture balance for your home.

7 Installation Safety

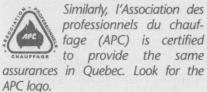
Support for Safe Wood Burning

Until the 1990s, stoves were not tested for safety, and homeowners had little or no guidance on installation. The result was house fires that were avoidable. Today, after years of co-operative efforts by all levels of government, the wood-heating industry and groups such as Fire Prevention Canada, several measures are in place to help you heat with wood – safely. These safety measures include the following:

- a reliable installation code ("CSA B365 Installation Code for Solid-Fuel-Burning Appliances and Equipment");

- safety-testing standards for stoves, inserts, fireplaces, furnaces, chimneys and flue pipes (almost all equipment for sale carries a certification label indicating that it conforms to safety tests); and

- a thorough training program for retailers, installers, chimney sweeps, municipal fire and building inspectors, and insurance inspectors (professionals in every part of Canada have completed the WETT or APC programs).

Today, wood-heating technology and its safe installation are more complicated. It isn't safe to simply hook up a wood stove to an existing chimney and begin using it for heating. You should get reliable advice from a trained professional and consider having the wood-burning system professionally installed. This way, you will get the best performance from the system and be assured of its safety. Before starting the installation, get a building permit from your municipal office and inform your insurance agent of your intentions.

The safest and most effective wood-heating system consists of a high-efficiency stove or fireplace certified by the EPA or CSA B415.1 and a suitable modern, certified venting system sized to match the appliance. When such a system is installed according to the manufacturer's instructions and safety codes, it will be as safe as any other home-heating option. At first, it will cost a little more than the older, out-of-date system. But its higher efficiency and lower maintenance costs mean you save every year and get a faster return on your investment.

When installed and used correctly, certified clean-burning appliances significantly reduce the risk of chimney fires. Their advanced combustion systems burn the smoke inside the firebox, so less creosote forms in the chimney. As a bonus, you save on chimney-cleaning costs, which can be significant for conventional systems that need cleaning two or three times each heating season.

Product Testing and Certification Agencies

These three agencies test wood-burning appliances for safety in Canada:

 CSA International (formerly the Canadian Standards Association)

 Underwriters' Laboratories of Canada

 Intertek Testing Services, Ltd. (formerly Warnock Hersey Professional Services Ltd.)

Certified appliances carry a label with the logo of the certification agency. They are your assurance that the product has been tested and conforms to safety standards.

As part of the certification process, the manufacturer's installation instructions are checked and approved. They must also contain certain basic information and messages. You can rely on these certified installation instructions to be accurate. When followed, they will result in a safe installation. Look for these logos when you are shopping for a wood-burning appliance.

Planning a Space Heater Installation

If you want your wood-burning space heater to make a large contribution to your home's total heating needs, do some planning before you select the heater and decide on its location. Whether you choose an advanced combustion wood stove, a pellet stove, a high-efficiency fireplace, a fireplace insert or a masonry heater, you should consider the same issues.

Put the Appliance Where You Live

Choosing the right location for the space heater may be the most important installation decision you make. Put the heater in the part of the house that you want to be the warmest. This is usually the main floor area – kitchen, living room and dining room – where family members spend most of their time. By locating the space heater here, you will be warm and comfortable while you eat meals and relax in the evenings.

Don't Put the Appliance in the Basement

The basement isn't usually a good place for space heating unless you are living there. Although some of the heated air from the stove does rise to higher levels of the house, it doesn't do so effectively. And usually, in an effort to keep the main-floor living spaces warm, the basement becomes over-heated. This wastes fuel, and the constant high firing can damage the stove's internal components.

An unfinished basement with poorly insulated walls and floor is a particularly bad location for a wood-burning space heater. The walls and floor absorb much of the heat, which is lost to the outside.

Also, space heaters operating in basements may over-fire or smoulder without anyone noticing. Finally, putting a stove in the basement can cause venting and indoor air quality problems.

The basement is a good location for a space heater only if your family spends a lot of time in a recreation room there. A basement space heater should have its chimney inside the house envelope.

Balance Stove Output With Room Size

The layout of your house can affect your choice of an appliance. If the house has small and separate rooms, you probably can't heat it well with a single space heater. A stove that is too large for the room where it is installed can make the room uncomfortably warm. A small space heater, however, can supplement your heating needs, while avoiding overheating the area.

Houses of open-plan design with fewer separations between rooms are the easiest to heat effectively with a space heater. In this situation, you can use a somewhat larger appliance without overheating the space, and the heat can flow to other rooms.

An experienced wood-burning appliance retailer is often your best source of advice on appliance sizing for your home. When you visit a store to look over the options, take along the blueprints or a floor plan of your house. This will save time and help the salesperson give you better advice.

Consider the Chimney Location

The chimney type, location and arrangement have a lot to do with how effectively a wood-burning system functions. When you are planning where to put the space heater, consider where you can route the chimney. If possible, avoid running the chimney up the outside wall of the house. A chimney always works best when it runs straight up from the appliance through the warm house interior. You can learn more about chimney location and performance in Chapter 9, "The Chimney."

Consider Heat Distribution

Whether or not a stove or fireplace has an internal fan, the heat from a space heater eventually rises to the ceiling of the room in which it is located. Heat collecting at this level tends to flow gradually through open stairwells to higher levels of the home. If there is no opening, the heat can stay close to the ceiling, while your feet are left cold.

A ceiling fan, slowly circulating air toward the floor, helps improve the overall effectiveness of the space heater. At the same time, it distributes the heat more evenly throughout the house. Fans are particularly effective in rooms with cathedral ceilings or in homes without central forced-air heating systems.

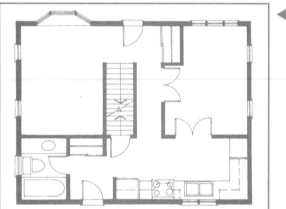

CLOSED FLOOR PLAN – A house with many enclosed rooms can be hard to heat with a single space heater. However, a properly located small space heater can heat much of the house if there is a way to move heat to other areas.

OPEN FLOOR PLAN – A house with an open design has few walls to separate rooms on the main floor. You can usually heat it effectively with a wood-burning space heater, if you put it in the right place.

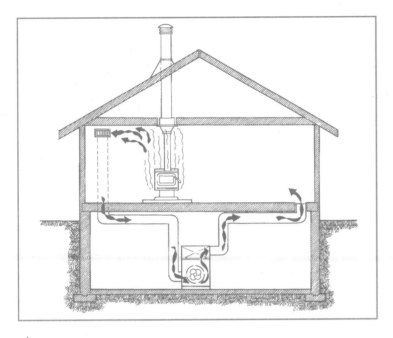

▲ *USING A FURNACE FAN TO DISTRIBUTE HEAT – A central furnace fan on low speed slowly circulates the air in the house and distributes the heat from the wood stove to other areas.*

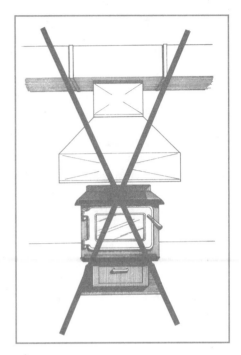

▲ *CAUTION – Never try to use a wood stove as a central furnace by putting a hood over the stove and connecting a furnace duct to the hood. This violates building codes and disrupts the air-circulating system. It can also cause the stove to spill smoke by depressurizing the room. The biggest danger?* **The chimney flow can reverse, filling your house with smoke and posing the risk of asphyxiation while you and your family are sleeping.**

One of the best ways to distribute heat from a wood stove is to use the air-circulating fan of a central furnace. By running the furnace fan on low speed, the air is gradually mixed and distributed throughout the house.

If you plan to build a new home, consider having your heating contractor install extra cold air return grilles on the wall at ceiling level in the room with the stove. Since the heated air from the stove will rise to the ceiling, the grilles don't need to be close to the stove in order to pick up and circulate the heated air around the house. It is, however, important to balance the flow of air into and out of the room through the ducts and registers. This way, when the furnace fan operates, the room will not become depressurized; this vacuum-type effect sucks air out of the house, pulling indoor air elsewhere.

In any case, most furnace fans use a lot of electricity on low speed. A better way is buying a furnace with a high-efficiency electronically commutated motor (ECM).

Another useful fan is the small accessory fan designed to hang in the upper corner of an open doorway. It helps move heat down a hallway or into the next room. Finally, installing grilles in floors and walls to allow air to flow passively into other rooms or levels helps distribute heat from a wood stove.

Installing Wood Stoves

The guidelines for installing wood stoves can be grouped into two categories. The first category is for stoves that have been tested and certified as meeting Canadian safety standards. The tests determined the lowest clearances and other installation guidelines for the specific appliance. You can find this information in the manufacturer's instructions. All new advanced wood stoves for sale in Canada today have been safety certified, and most insurance companies will accept only certified appliances.

The second category is for appliances that haven't been tested and certified. These include used or antique stoves, most stoves built before the early 1980s and stoves built by small, informal welding shops. There are several good reasons to avoid uncertified appliances.

- They are less efficient than new, certified appliances, so you will burn more wood to get the same amount of heat, which will produce high levels of smoke and creosote.

- They require larger installation clearances than new certified stoves, making them more difficult and expensive to install.

- Installation rules for uncertified stoves are so complicated that you will need an experienced professional to interpret them or to install your stove.

- The construction quality and convenience features of new certified stoves are superior to older, uncertified stoves.

- Uncertified stoves may constitute a serious fire hazard.

- You may not be able to get insurance, even at a high rate.

You can find guidelines for installing these uncertified stoves in the solid-fuel-burning installation code, CSA B365. The lowest clearances to combustible materials for uncertified stoves are large – 1200 mm (48 in.) for radiant stoves and 900 mm (36 in.) for stoves surrounded by jackets behind which convection air can flow.

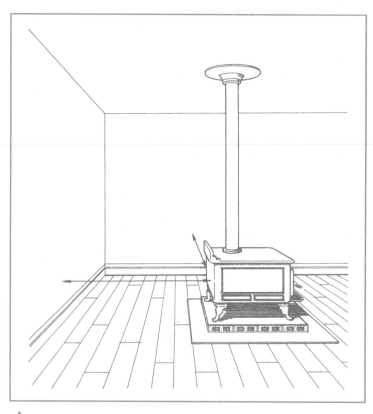

▲ *Side and Rear Wall Clearance for an Uncertified Stove – The manufacturer's installation instructions specify the right clearances for the appliance. The clearances for certified appliances vary, but are less than those shown in the following table (from CSA B365) for uncertified appliances. Many of the new, certified appliances have heat shields on the sides and rear, reducing clearances by as much as 90 percent.*

Clearances to Combustible Material for Appliances Using Solid Fuel

Source: CSA International B365-01, Table 2

Application	Minimum clearance, mm (in.)		
	Top	Sides, rear and corner	Fuelling and ash removal side(s)
Appliances with no shielding*	1500 (60)	1200 (48)	1200 (48)
Appliances with shielding*	1500 (60)	900 (36)	1200 (48)

* Shielding consists of protection such as external jacketing or a metal heat shield attached to the sides and rear of the appliance and spaced out at least 50 mm (2 in.) by non-combustible spacers, with provision for air circulation at bottom and top.

Note: Clearances shall be measured from the outer surface of the appliance to the combustible material; a non-combustible covering applied over the combustible material shall be disregarded.

Reduce Minimum Clearances Safely

Like most homeowners, you probably want your wood stove to take up as little floor space as possible. As a result, heat shields are often used to reduce clearances and protect walls and ceilings. Some stove manufacturers offer certified accessory shields with their products to provide reduced wall clearance. If you aren't offered accessory shields for your stove or if you want to reduce the clearance even further, you can buy effective wall and ceiling shields or have them built.

You can safely reduce the clearances for both **certified** and **uncertified** stoves by following the rules set out in standard CSA B365. The common feature of the clearance reduction rules is air space behind the shield material. This space sets up a convection flow of air when the stove is operating and prevents the stove's heat from reaching the wall. (The percentage shown in the table on page 26 is the amount by which you can reduce the lowest clearance with the particular shield system listed.) By using heat shields, you can reduce wall and ceiling clearances.

Clearance-reducing shields are made from various materials, from simple sheet metal to more decorative brick, stone slices or ceramic tiles. Although CSA B365 allows you to make shields from solid brick, this isn't practical because they are expensive and hard to build. You can achieve the same visual effect for less money by using brick slices, rather than full bricks. In addition, shields must be permanently mounted to walls – free-standing panels aren't acceptable as clearance-reducing shields.

Rules for constructing heat shields

- Minimum space between shield and combustible material: 21 mm ($^7/_8$ in.).

- Minimum clearance along bottom of shield: 25 mm (1 in.).

- Maximum clearance along bottom of shield: 75 mm (3 in.).

- Minimum clearance along top of shield at ceiling: 75 mm (3 in.).

- Shield extension beyond each side of appliance: 45 cm (18 in.).

- Shield extension above appliance: 50 cm (20 in.).

- Edge clearance for ceiling shields: 75 mm (3 in.).

- Glues used in shield construction must not ignite or lose adhesive qualities at temperatures likely to be reached.

- Mounting hardware must allow full vertical ventilation.

- Mounting hardware must not be located closer than 200 mm (8 in.) from the vertical centre line of the appliance.

- Mounting hardware that extends from the shield surface into combustibles may be used only at the lateral extremities of the shield.

Reducing Clearances with Shielding

Source: CSA 365-01, Table 3, Reduction in Appliance and Ductwork Clearance from Combustible Material with Specified Forms of Protection

	Clearances may be reduced by these percentages	
Type of protection (shield)	**Sides and rear %**	**Top %**
Sheet metal, a minimum of 29 gauge in thickness spaced out at least 21 mm (⁷⁄₈ in.) by non-combustible spacers	67	50
Ceramic tiles or equivalent non-combustible material on non-combustible supports spaced out at least 21 mm (⁷⁄₈ in.) by non-combustible spacers	50	33
Ceramic tiles or equivalent non-combustible material on non-combustible supports with a minimum of 29 gauge sheet metal backing spaced out at least 21 mm (⁷⁄₈ in.) by non-combustible spacers	67	50
Brick spaced out at least 21 mm (⁷⁄₈ in.) by non-combustible spacers	50	n/a
Brick with a minimum of 29 gauge sheet metal backing spaced out at least 21 mm (⁷⁄₈ in.) by non-combustible spacers	67	n/a

You can also reduce minimum clearances by using commercial shields. They are tested to determine how effectively they can reduce clearances. The shields are certified and carry a label that confirms they have passed the tests and provides details on clearance reduction. Some commercial shields can be attached directly to combustible walls without needing an air space.

The first step in reducing clearances is to determine the lowest clearance, from either the stove label or the Table of Clearances for Uncertified Stoves (from the CSA B365 installation code). Then calculate the amount the clearance will be reduced with the type of shield you plan to use (from the table on clearance reduction).

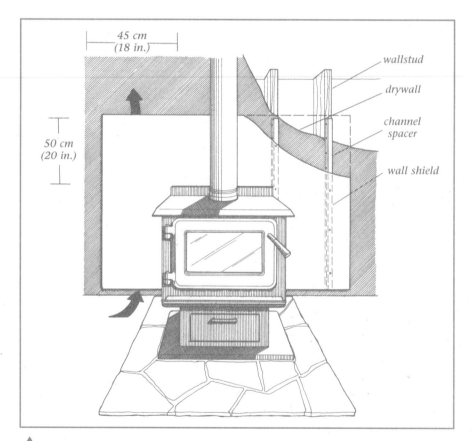

45 cm (18 in.)

50 cm (20 in.)

wallstud

drywall

channel spacer

wall shield

▲ *Cut-away of Wall Shield Assembly – By allowing air to flow between the shield and the combustible surface, a wall shielding assembly can safely reduce minimum clearances. The shield must extend at least 50 cm (20 in.) above the top of the appliance and 45 cm (18 in.) beyond each edge of the appliance.*

Channel spacers are the most effective type because they give good support to the shield and don't transmit heat through the mounting hardware to the combustible wall. Metal wall strapping, available from most building supply stores, is made of light steel channels that work well as shield spacers. Note that the bottom of the channel is notched to allow cooling air to enter. The shield must extend 45 cm (18 in.) beyond each edge of the appliance and 50 cm (20 in.) above the top of the appliance.

Parts of the Wood Stove Installation

A typical wood stove installation consists of the following components, starting at floor level:

- a non-combustible floor pad to protect flooring or carpets from embers that might fall from the stove during loading or ash removal;

- a wood stove;

- a flue pipe that connects the flue collar of the stove to the chimney; and

- a chimney system that produces the draft that draws combustion air into the stove and expels the exhaust gases to the outside.

Each part of the space heater system deserves careful attention during installation in order to produce effective heating.

Protect the floor

Certified wood stoves will not overheat a combustible floor. During safety testing, the floor temperature is checked and must not exceed safe limits. Although the floor won't overheat during normal operation, you still need to protect it from live embers that might fall from the stove as you tend the fire or remove ashes. The floor pad must be a durable, non-combustible material, such as sheet metal, grouted ceramic tile or mortared brick. Floor pads must normally extend **not less** than 45 cm (18 in.) in front of the loading door and 20 cm (8 in.) beyond the other sides and the back. Don't install the floor pad on a carpet unless the pad is structurally supported so that it doesn't move, crack or distort.

Uncertified stoves haven't passed safety tests, so heat from the bottom may overheat floors or cause a fire. These appliances have different rules for floor protection, depending on the height of the stove legs and any bottom protection the stove might have. If you are installing an uncertified appliance, contact a qualified professional for details. Better yet, choose a new, certified stove – especially a highly efficient model.

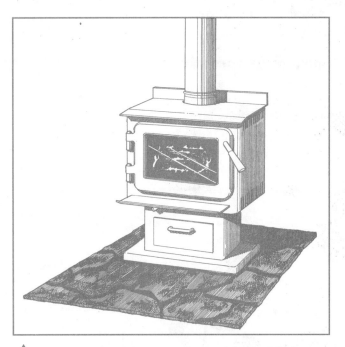

▲ *NON-COMBUSTIBLE FLOOR PAD SIZE AND TYPE – The floor pad protects flooring from hot embers or ashes that might fall from the stove as you fill it or tend the fire. The pad must extend at least 20 cm (8 in.) beyond the sides and rear, and 45 cm (18 in.) in front of the loading door. Also, the floor pad must be a continuous, non-combustible surface. Do not mount the floor pad on carpet, unless the pad is strong enough to resist bending or cracking.*

Installing flue pipes

Flue pipes carry the exhaust gases from the stove flue collar to the base of the chimney. They have been called the weak link in the wood-burning system, because they are often improperly installed. As you will see from the list below, several rules exist for safely installing flue pipe assemblies. They apply to flue pipes connected to all wood-burning appliances, including central heating systems.

Flue pipe assemblies should be as short and as direct as possible between the stove and the entrance to the chimney. This reduces heat loss and promotes a strong and reliable chimney draft. The ideal assembly rises straight up from the stove flue collar and fits directly into the chimney without elbows or curves. A straight flue pipe assembly allows the most gas flow and results in a stronger draft. Straight assemblies also need less maintenance because there are no corners where creosote deposits can accumulate.

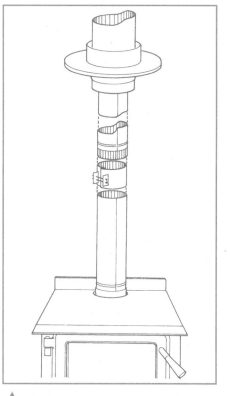

▲ *THE IDEAL SINGLE-WALL FLUE PIPE ASSEMBLY – When the flue gas path is straight, the system produces a stronger draft and needs less maintenance than an assembly with elbows. The ideal flue pipe assembly rises straight from the appliance flue collar into the chimney. A straight single-wall flue pipe assembly needs an inspection wrap or telescopic section so that you can install and remove it without having to move the appliance. The wrap also allows some movement for expansion when the flue pipe gets hot.*

Rules for single-wall flue pipe assemblies

- Minimum clearance from combustible material: 45 cm (18 in.).

- The minimum clearance may be cut in half to 22.5 cm (9 in.) if suitable shielding is installed either on the pipe or the combustible surface.

- Maximum overall length of straight pipe: 3 m (10 ft.).

- Maximum unsupported horizontal length: 1 m (3 ft.).

- Maximum combined change in direction: 180 degrees (i.e. not more than two 90-degree elbows).

- Minimum upward slope towards the chimney: 2 cm/m ($\frac{1}{4}$ in. per ft.).

- The crimped ends (male) of the sections must be oriented toward the appliance.

- Each joint in the assembly must be fastened with at least three screws, including the connections at the appliance flue collar and chimney.

- Flue pipes that are 15, 17.5 and 20 cm (6, 7 and 8 in.) in diameter must have at least 24 gauge thickness.

- Don't use galvanized flue pipes – the coatings vaporize at high temperatures and release dangerous gases. Use black-painted flue pipes.

- The assembly, including the elbows, must have allowance for expansion: straight assemblies should include either an inspection wrap with one end unfastened or a telescopic section.

Certified double-wall flue pipe systems are also available. These systems are tested to determine the minimum clearance at which they can be installed. You will find the clearance information on the labels attached to the pipe and in the manufacturer's installation instructions.

The lowest clearances for installing certified double-wall flue pipes are less than those for single-wall pipes. Also, the maximum length of a double-wall pipe assembly may be greater than is permitted for a single-wall pipe. This extra length is useful for installations in rooms with cathedral ceilings, because the distance to the base of the chimney may exceed 3 m (10 ft.).

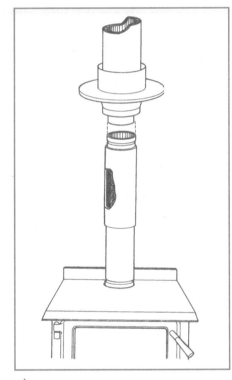

▲ *Double-wall Flue Pipe Assemblies – Certified double-wall flue pipes have a stainless-steel inner liner and a sealed or ventilated outer shell. They cost more than single-wall pipes, but last longer and produce a more stable assembly. You can place double-wall pipes closer to combustible materials than single-wall pipes.*

The two general types of double-wall flue pipes are sealed and vented. A **sealed double-wall flue pipe** retains heat in the flue gases because the air space between the inner liner and outer shell acts as an insulator. A sealed pipe is a good choice for most installations, particularly if the assembly must be long or if the appliance is expected to produce low flue gas temperatures. These pipes can improve the draft and reduce creosote deposits.

Vented double-wall flue pipes release more heat into the room as the gases flow through, by allowing cooling air to pass between the inner and outer layers, removing heat from the inner surface. This can cause too much creosote to form and create a poor draft. You may need to put the flue pipe a bit closer to a combustible surface. Partially shielded flue pipes, which have a curved shield at the back towards the wall and expose the single-wall liner to the room, are a simple solution.

Installing Advanced Combustion, High-Efficiency Fireplaces

Advanced combustion fireplaces are installed within the structure of the house and surrounded by combustible building materials. The fireplace and its heating flow paths, chimney and other components are safety tested together as a unit. Therefore, you can install only the chimney and the other components that the fireplace was tested with. No general instructions exist for installing such fireplaces; each fireplace design has its own installation guidelines, which you can find in the manufacturer's instruction manual.

Once you find an advanced fireplace you like, ask the retailer for a copy of the installation instructions. Study them at home so you can become familiar with the fireplace before making your decision. The manual will tell you about safe clearances, mantel heights, limitations on decorative finishing materials and guidelines for routing and installing remote heating ducts. Spending some time getting to know the product is worthwhile, even if you plan to hire professional technicians to install the fireplace.

The back of the fireplace and its heating paths and chimney will be enclosed and out of sight once the installation is completed. So it is important to follow the manufacturer's instructions exactly to ensure that clearances are adequate. Installing an advanced factory-built fireplace is complicated and not a do-it-yourself job – unless you have plenty of carpentry experience and are willing to invest the time to ensure you get every part of the installation just right. A better option is to contract an experienced wood-heat technician to install the unit for you.

Installing Fireplace Inserts and Hearth-Mount Stoves

One rule that applies to all fireplace inserts is that a full, stainless-steel chimney liner must be installed from the insert flue collar to the top of the chimney. The liner reduces the size of the chimney flue to match that of the insert collar and isolates the flue gas from the masonry structure. This retains heat and produces a stronger draft. The liner also makes cleaning and servicing easier, since it can be cleaned from the top of the chimney, and the deposits can be removed from inside the insert. With a full liner, you don't have to remove the insert for cleaning, a costly procedure that can damage the hearth.

A fireplace insert or hearth-mount stove and its full chimney liner are, in effect, permanently installed. Usually, you must alter the structure of the masonry fireplace to complete the installation, and it may not be possible to return it to its original condition if you change your mind later.

When an insert or hearth mount is installed in a fireplace, you almost always need to extend the hearth at least 45 cm (18 in.) beyond the front of the appliance to protect the floor. This hearth extension must be permanently mounted to the floor. Fire-retardant hearth rugs aren't considered adequate floor protection. The installation instructions may also specify a minimum mantel height above the insert. If your fireplace mantel is lower, you may need to shield it so that it doesn't overheat.

Although installing a fireplace insert may appear straightforward, it isn't a simple do-it-yourself job. Before installation, the existing fireplace and chimney must be cleaned thoroughly so that no combustible deposits remain. Installing the liner can be challenging, and the correct materials must be used. The connections to the insert and between liner sections must be secure, and all materials must be corrosion-resistant. Look for a dealer with years of experience installing inserts. Professional installers know the trouble spots and how to avoid future problems.

Installing Masonry Heaters

Masonry heaters are entirely different in design, construction and operation from conventional masonry fireplaces. The core of the heater, consisting of the firebox and heat exchanger, has a series of precast components made of high-temperature brick materials. They are assembled by a mason and surrounded by the finish material (brick, tile or stone). The clearances of a masonry heater from combustible materials must meet the standards found in building codes for conventional fireplaces.

Someone without specialized training and plenty of experience would find it difficult to build a masonry heater that would perform well and last a long time. A masonry heater is not only costly but also a lifetime investment, so select your heater mason carefully. Ask for references from previous customers, and call them for their comments. Qualified heater masons are certified by the Masonry Heater Association of North America.

Installing Pellet-Burning Appliances

You can find the installation guidelines for certified pellet-burning appliances in the manufacturer's instructions. The manual provides details of clearances, the materials used to vent the exhaust and the arrangement of vent components.

Almost all pellet stoves use a small fan to force the exhaust through the venting system, so they do not rely on natural chimney draft for normal operation. Also, since the fuel and air mixture can be adjusted and set once the unit is burning cleanly, the fire in a pellet stove is unlikely to smoulder and produce creosote. For these reasons, pellet stoves don't need the high-temperature chimneys that wood stoves do. Instead, they can use a lightweight double-wall pipe called a pellet vent. Some pellet stoves can be vented horizontally out through a wall, so you don't need a chimney.

However, there are some drawbacks to straight horizontal pellet vent installations. First, the vent must be far from windows and doors to keep the exhaust smell from getting into the house – a location that may be difficult to find. Second, pellet stove exhaust fans aren't powerful. If a strong wind blows against the vent wall, exhaust can be forced back into the house. And third, the stove may smoke into the house if the power fails, because there is no natural draft to draw it outside.

Experienced pellet-stove installers often recommend venting the stove vertically up through the roof. At the least, they install some vertical rise, so that you have enough natural draft to draw the smoke outside during a power failure.

Since the exhaust fan puts pellet stove vents under positive pressure, seal each joint carefully with high-temperature sealant. This will prevent fine ash and soot particles from leaking into the room. It is a good idea to have a new pellet stove professionally installed and adjusted to burn properly. Annual servicing by the dealer to ensure that the system is reliable is also a good investment.

Installing Central Heating Furnaces and Boilers

When considering central heating with wood, a reputable heating retailer or contractor is your best source of information on available systems and their suitability for your home. Since installing central heating appliances is complicated and requires several specialized skills, you must hire professionals to do the work.

Combination wood-oil, wood-electric and add-on furnaces are the most popular central wood-heating options installed in basement furnace rooms. The controls and duct systems are linked, so the heat distribution system is shared by both energy sources. A certified wood-burning add-on furnace can share a chimney with an oil furnace, provided the chimney is suited for use with a wood-burning furnace. However, if coupled with a gas furnace, the add-on must have a separate chimney.

All wood-burning furnaces and boilers must be certified to meet the CSA International safety test standard. Installation details are determined during testing. As a result, the installation rules for each make and model of central heating furnace or boiler differ somewhat. The specific information can be found in the manufacturer's installation instructions.

If you do decide to go with an uncertified outdoor boiler, the installation should be done by an experienced dealer. Get references and speak to other owners of outdoor boilers before making the decision and choosing the dealer. With an installed cost as high as $10,000, an outdoor boiler is a big investment. Make sure your dealer has plenty of experience and a good reputation.

8 Your Installation Checklist

Before the System Is Installed

- Call your municipal building department to discuss your plans and find out if you need a building permit. In some municipalities, you need a permit to exchange an old stove for a new one.

- Contact your insurance agent to find out if the installation will affect your policy. Many insurance companies add surcharges to policies on houses with wood-burning equipment. If you think the quote is high, shop around – especially if you are having a high-efficiency combustion unit installed by a WETT- or APC-certified technician. Some insurance companies reduce or eliminate surcharges if the system is installed by a certified professional and the appliance is an advanced technology model.

- Make sure the installer has general liability and errors and omissions insurance.

- Review the installation plans with your retailer, installer or contractor. Make sure you understand what is involved and what all the costs will be. If you are installing the system yourself, get advice from a trained professional so that you don't misinterpret or overlook any key safety issues.

- Read the manufacturer's installation instructions carefully.

While the System Is Being Installed

- Make sure that the manufacturer's instructions are being followed exactly. If the installer deviates from the instructions, ask why. Any variation from the installation guidelines should be reviewed by a third party such as a building inspector.

After the Installation Is Completed

- Check the installation to be sure that it meets code requirements.

- Have your municipal building or fire department inspect the installation. Some departments are reluctant to inspect wood-heating systems. In some cases, these departments will refer you to a local WETT- or APC-certified retailer, installer or chimney sweep for the inspection.

- Notify your insurance agent. Your insurance company may send someone to inspect your installation.

- Install smoke detectors on or near the ceiling at the exits to the room where the appliance is installed. Replace the batteries annually, and consider installing a carbon monoxide detector.

- Buy a labelled and approved ABC-type fire extinguisher, and store it near the installation. Follow the instructions on the extinguisher label for maintenance procedures.

- Read and follow the manufacturer's operating instructions.

9 The Chimney

Modern, efficient appliances need modern, efficient chimneys. The selection, location and installation of the chimney are as important as the type of wood-burning appliance you choose. A properly designed and installed chimney will provide many years of reliable service and allow your appliance to perform correctly.

How Chimneys Work

An effective chimney is an important part of any successful wood-burning system. Many of the reported problems with the performance of wood-burning appliances can be traced to the chimney. Knowing how chimneys work is not only necessary in selecting the correct type and designing the installation, but also useful in operating your wood-burning system from day to day.

MINIMUM CHIMNEY HEIGHT ABOVE THE ROOF – *The top of a chimney should be high enough to be above the air turbulence caused when wind blows against the house and its roof. The chimney must extend at least 1 m (3 ft.) above the highest point of contact with the roof, and at least 60 cm (2 ft.) higher than any roof line or obstacle within a horizontal distance of 3 m (10 ft.).*

Chimneys operate on the principle that hot air rises above cold air – thus, the hot gas in a chimney rises because it is less dense than the air outside the house. The rising gas creates a pressure difference called **draft**, which draws combustion air into the appliance and expels the exhaust gas outside through the chimney. The hotter the gas compared with the air outside, the stronger the draft. In this chapter, you will also learn that a chimney should produce a small amount of draft even when no fire is burning. In fact, some of the most serious flaws in chimney performance are revealed when the appliance is not being used.

The chimney's function is to produce the draft that draws combustion air into the appliance and safely exhaust the gases from combustion to the outside. To fulfil this role, the chimney must do the following:

- isolate nearby combustible materials from flue gas heat;

- tolerate the high gas temperatures caused by overfiring and chimney fires;

- conserve flue gas heat to produce a strong and consistent draft;

- resist corrosion and weather effects; and

- be well sealed to prevent leakage.

Guidelines for Installing Chimneys

1) Install the chimney within the house envelope, rather than up an outside wall. Chimneys along an outside wall are exposed to wind and low temperatures; this chilling effect can reduce the available draft to the appliance and cause condensation. Outside chimneys also tend to create a cold backdraft when no fire is burning. This allows cold air and odours to enter the house and makes it hard to light a fire without getting smoke in the house. On the other hand, chimneys that run up inside the house benefit from being enclosed within a warm environment. Inside chimneys produce stronger draft and accumulate less creosote when a fire is burning. They usually produce a small amount of draft, even when there is no fire.

2) Building codes require that the top of the chimney extends at least 1 m (3 ft.) above the point where it exits the roof. It should also be at

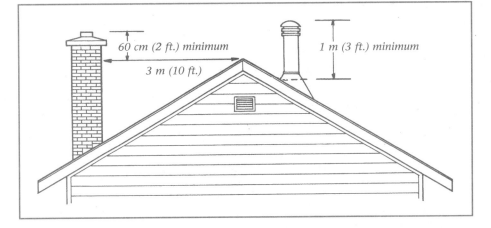

60 cm (2 ft.) minimum

3 m (10 ft.)

1 m (3 ft.) minimum

least 60 cm (2 ft.) higher than any roof, building or other obstacle within a horizontal distance of 3 m (10 ft.). These rules are intended to place the top of the chimney higher than any areas of air turbulence caused by wind. In practice, chimneys must sometimes be raised even higher than these minimums in order to avoid air turbulence caused by nearby obstacles, such as trees or other houses.

3) The most important factor in chimney draft is temperature difference. If you experience draft problems, increase flue gas temperature by doing one or more of the following:

- burn smaller, hotter fires to avoid smouldering;

- keep the flue pipe assembly as short and straight as possible (try not to use right angles);

- use a sealed double-wall flue pipe;

- re-line a masonry chimney;

- re-install the chimney inside the house; or

- construct an enclosure or chase around an outside chimney.

4) The chimney flue should be the same size as the appliance flue collar. In the past, many chimneys were too large for the appliance they served. But bigger is not better when it comes to chimney size. Flue gas flows faster and has less time to lose heat in a smaller chimney flue. In planning

wood-heating systems, some experienced installers even choose a chimney that has a smaller inside diameter than the appliance flue collar. They usually do this when the chimney runs inside the house and is fairly tall. Chimneys taller than 8 m (about 26 ft.) sometimes produce more draft than the appliance needs, so a smaller-diameter chimney doesn't reduce performance. Only an experienced technician should decide whether the flue should be smaller than the appliance flue collar.

5) Taller chimneys produce stronger draft. A rule of thumb is that the entire system (from the floor on which the appliance is mounted to the top of the chimney) must be at least 4.6 m (15 ft.) high. Most installations are taller than this, but those in cottages with shallow-pitch roofs or in single-storey buildings with flat roofs may not. If you experience draft problems with a short system, consider adding to the chimney's height. However, if your chimney runs up the outside wall of the house, making it taller may not improve draft, because the extra heat loss cancels out any benefit.

Suitable Chimney Options

Two general categories of chimneys are approved for use with wood-burning appliances: the 650°C factory-built chimney and the masonry chimney.

The 650°C Factory-Built Chimney

This type of chimney was developed to withstand the high temperatures produced by a chimney fire. It features better insulation than other factory-built chimneys to isolate nearby combustible material from the high gas temperatures in the flue when a fire is burning. At the same time, this increased insulation keeps flue gases and inner flue surfaces warmer. As a result, less creosote forms in the chimney, reducing the risk of chimney fire significantly.

Specific types of factory-built metal chimneys can be used with wood-burning appliances. Wood stoves, wood-burning central heating furnaces and some factory-built fireplaces must use the 650°C metal chimney, approved to Underwriters' Laboratories of Canada (ULC) standard S629. The 650°C refers to the continuous gas temperature for which it is designed; it is higher than for chimneys intended for other fuels. Most, but not all, 650°C chimneys have 5 cm (2 in.) of insulation between the inner liner and outer shell.

The 650°C chimneys were developed in the early 1980s because earlier chimney designs couldn't withstand the heat from a

▲ *Factory-built chimney*

The Masonry Chimney

A conventional masonry chimney consists of a clay tile liner surrounded by a structure of brick, block or stone. Stainless-steel liners can be installed in masonry chimneys to correct internal damage caused by a chimney fire. A qualified chimney sweep should inspect your existing masonry chimney before your wood-burning appliance is installed.

Masonry chimneys that are built according to the guidelines found in all building codes may be used with wood-burning appliances. If you are planning to have a masonry chimney built, get a building permit. And make it clear to the mason who will be doing the work that the chimney must conform to the building code.

Your masonry chimney will perform better if you build it with new materials rather than traditional ones. For example, you may wish to specify round flue tiles instead of the standard square or rectangular tiles. Round clay flue tiles with shiplap joints are also available. These joints give a better fit and help prevent smoke and moisture from leaking into the surrounding masonry. Alternatively, some brands of certified stainless-steel chimney liners are now approved for use in new chimney construction. Specialized, poured-in-place chimney liners are also available in some areas. A local chimney sweep can tell you if there is a contractor near you.

chimney fire. The 650°C chimney has better insulation and a stronger, more corrosion-resistant inner liner than the older types. This improved insulation isolates nearby combustible materials from high gas temperatures in the flue. The insulation also makes a chimney fire less likely to occur. By keeping flue gases warmer, less creosote forms in the chimney.

Most new factory-built fireplaces are approved for use with a special metal chimney that has a 25 mm (1 in.) wall thickness, but has the same upgraded liner found in the 650°C type. Your wood-heating retailer can show you the differences between these chimney types and which one you will need. All factory-built chimneys must have the proper chimney cap installed to produce reliable draft, to prevent water from leaking in and to comply with the manufacturer's installation instructions.

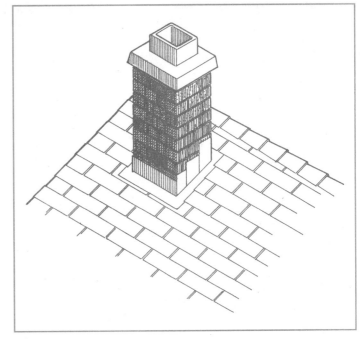

▲ *Masonry chimney*

One important feature often missing from masonry chimneys is a proper rain cap. The name may imply that it just keeps rain out of the flue, but it has another key role – it helps prevent smoking and other draft problems caused by the wind. When wind flows down toward the open top of a chimney, it produces a positive pressure zone. This works against chimney draft and forces the exhaust back down the chimney. Even when wind flows horizontally toward a chimney, its normal turbulence can produce pressure that opposes or increases chimney draft. Every chimney, regardless of its design or materials, should have a cap to reduce wind-related venting failures or disruptions.

To have your existing masonry chimney checked, your best option is to hire a qualified chimney sweep. If you see any deterioration of the bricks or mortar joints near the top of the chimney, dark stains or white deposits on the brick work, pieces of tile or liquid stains at the chimney clean-out, or brick faces splitting off outside, have the chimney inspected and repaired immediately.

Masonry chimneys that have been damaged by a chimney fire, or that are too large for your appliance, can be re-lined with a certified, stainless-steel liner. The liner can have either a rigid or corrugated flex design.

Unsuitable Chimneys

Type A Chimneys – This type of metal chimney, used before 1983, is not suitable or acceptable for wood-burning appliances under building code guidelines. This chimney was designed for oil furnaces, which is how it is mainly used today. Type A chimneys cannot withstand the high temperatures of chimney fires.

Type A chimneys normally had a 25 mm (1 in.) wall thickness and were available with either round or square outer casings. If your wood-burning system uses a Type A chimney, consider upgrading to the new 650°C chimney as soon as possible. If it cannot be changed right away, have your chimney cleaned and inspected by a certified chimney sweep to determine if it is still safe to use. Deteriorated metal chimneys can be hazardous.

Bracket Masonry Chimneys – The term "bracket chimney" refers to masonry chimneys that rest on wooden or brick supports within the wall of a house, rather than being supported on proper concrete foundations. Don't use bracket chimneys. They are potentially hazardous and cannot be upgraded to meet building code requirements. To comply with the codes, masonry chimneys need a foundation that extends below the frost line, which is a few metres below grade in most of Canada.

Unlined Masonry Chimneys – Masonry chimneys must have a liner made of clay tiles, firebrick or stainless steel to be suitable. You can upgrade some old, unlined chimneys by installing a certified stainless-steel liner.

Air-Cooled Chimneys – Some decorative factory-built fireplaces are approved for use with chimneys that use air flow, instead of solid insulation between inner and outer layers, to keep the outer surface cool. Never connect wood-burning heating appliances to air-cooled chimneys, or flue gas will cool excessively.

Creosote and Chimney Fires

When wood burns slowly – as it often does in a conventional, air-tight stove or furnace – it makes a smoky fire and produces more creosote deposits than a quick, hot fire does. Creosote is a highly flammable material. If it ignites near the base of the chimney, it can produce a raging fire that travels up the chimney, creating extremely high temperatures as it spreads. The high temperature can damage the clay liners in a masonry chimney or the metal liner in a factory-built chimney. Although 650°C chimneys can withstand these temperatures, the heat causes extreme stress in the chimney.

Chimney fires result from poor firing techniques combined with a lack of maintenance. If unseasoned wood (wood that hasn't been dried enough) is burned slowly in an old "airtight" heater, creosote can build up quickly and the risk of a chimney fire increases.

When you operate wood-burning appliances properly, some creosote may still be deposited, but it will be less combustible. Instead of the black, tarry, highly flammable creosote from smouldering fires, proper firing may create small amounts of soft, flaky and dark brown deposits.

You can prevent chimney fires. Have your chimney checked for creosote deposits regularly, until you find out how quickly it builds up in the system. Conventional wood heaters can produce creosote quickly because they can't burn the wood as completely as advanced combustion designs. In severe cases of smouldering, it may take only a few days for enough creosote to build up to sustain a chimney fire. The new, low-emission wood stoves burn the wood so completely that, when operated properly, their chimneys normally need cleaning only once a year.

Never assume that the chimney is clean. Check it regularly to be sure, especially during the spring and fall. If you do have a chimney fire, have the chimney inspected and repaired, if necessary, before using the system again. A chimney fire is a clear sign of a problem with the appliance, the fuel or the way the system is operated. Make changes to avoid chimney fires in the future.

Using an energy-efficient wood-burning appliance, coupled with good installation and proper burning techniques, dramatically lowers the chance of a chimney fire.

The smell of wood smoke inside your home is a sign that the wood-burning system isn't working properly. Smoke contains harmful air pollutants, which can be irritating or even dangerous in high concentrations. Wood-burning systems that are properly designed, installed and operated will not spill smoke into the house. If you have been using proper burning techniques, burning only dry wood, and still smell smoke in your home, have your system inspected.

Three Reasons Why Smoke Spills From Wood-Burning Systems

Poor System Design

Certain design characteristics can make a wood-burning system more likely to spill smoke. Most of them result in low flue temperatures and low draft. For example, chimneys that run up the outside wall of the house lose heat and produce weak draft. Long, single-walled flue pipe assemblies give up too much heat before the gases even reach the chimney. Each 90° elbow in the flue pipe assembly restricts and slows down the flow of gases. More than one elbow can restrict the flow enough to cause smoke spillage. Any of these characteristics may or may not cause smoke spillage on its own. However, when an outside chimney is combined with a long flue pipe assembly with several elbows, you will almost certainly have smoke spillage.

Negative Pressure in the House

Energy efficiency practices and new building codes are making new houses more and more airtight. The reduced air leakage makes houses more comfortable and easier to heat. But it can create problems if you use high-volume exhausts. For example, a powerful downdraft kitchen-range exhaust can force more air out of a new house than what leaks in through its tightly sealed walls.

Appliances such as high-grade bathroom or kitchen fans, clothes dryers and central vacuum cleaners can cause similar problems. When this happens, the pressure inside the house becomes negative compared to the outside, which works against chimney draft. In severe cases, this pressure draws smoke back down the chimney into the house. This reverse flow is most likely to happen as the fire dies down to a coal bed, when chimney draft is weakest.

You can avoid negative pressure problems in your new home by limiting the number, size and use of exhaust fans. Avoid running powerful fans such as a downdraft range exhaust while the wood-burning system is operating. If you can't avoid using the fan, link the exhaust system to a make-up fan that forces air into the house to replace the exhausted air. This keeps the house pressure close to neutral. Contact your wood-heating retailer or heating contractor for details on make-up air systems.

Building codes cover the potential for excessive depressurization of airtight new houses. Two options are normally permitted to ensure good indoor air quality:

- installing a make-up air system to compensate for the air exhausted from the house; or

- installing a carbon monoxide detector in the room containing the wood-burning system to detect and warn of spillage.

Your wood-heating retailer or municipal building department can explain the local rules.

Improper Appliance-Firing Technique

One of the most common reasons for smoke spillage is a smouldering fire. A wood fire that is starved for air will smoulder, and the exhaust temperature will fall too low to produce enough draft. If you open the loading door during a smouldering fire, smoke will spill into the room. Even when the loading door is closed, severe smouldering can produce smoke spillage, which can be hazardous when it happens during the night. By using the suggestions on proper firing techniques found in Chapter 12, "Burning Wood Efficiently," you will be able to build effective fires and prevent smouldering.

Does Outdoor Air Reduce Smoke Spillage?

It has been widely believed that you could reduce or eliminate smoke spillage by supplying outdoor air through a duct, either directly to the appliance's combustion chamber or indirectly to the room in which the appliance is located. However, research shows that outdoor air supplies may not work. Smoke spillage occurs at the same level of room depressurization, whether or not an outdoor air duct is installed. The same research shows that wind effects around the house can reverse the flow in these ducts, which may create a fire hazard if the duct is connected directly to the combustion chamber.

Some building codes require that you provide wood-burning fireplaces with outdoor combustion air. You must comply with this requirement, but be aware that performance will not improve. And take steps to protect combustible materials around the duct from overheating if the gas flow reverses.

Is Your House Acting Like a Chimney?

An operating chimney is an enclosed column of warm air or gases surrounded by colder outside air. The warm air or gas in the chimney is more buoyant than the dense, cold outside air so it rises. This produces the draft in the chimney.

In winter, your house is also an enclosed column of warm, buoyant air creating a form of draft. In effect, the warm air creates higher air pressures as it pushes toward the top of the house. At the same time, the pressure in the basement is lower than the pressure outside. This is why the basement of a leaky house feels drafty and the rooms on the second floor are more comfortable – the cold outside air is drawn into the area of lower pressure. The difference in pressure at various levels of the house is called **stack effect**. It can cause venting problems and smoke spillage when it competes with a chimney that serves a wood-burning appliance in the basement.

Some houses act more like chimneys than others. Two- or three-storey houses produce more of a stack effect than bungalows because they have a taller column of warm air. A house with most of its leaks or open windows at the upper levels tends to produce more of a stack effect because the leaks offer a ready path for warm air to escape (like the open top of a chimney). Outside chimneys connected to heating appliances in the basement can backdraft if the stack effect is strong enough. This allows cold outside air – or smoke and/or carbon monoxide if there is a smouldering fire in the appliance – to spill into the house.

The stack effect is particularly troublesome when an appliance served by an outside chimney is installed in a single-storey section of a two-storey house (as shown in the illustration below). When no fire is burning in the stove, the chimney can't produce as much standby draft as the house produces in the stack effect because the chimney is shorter and colder.

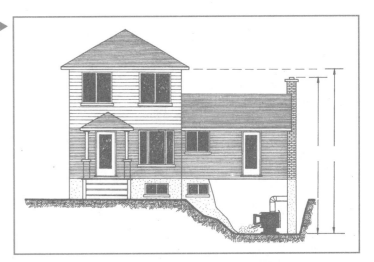

PROBLEM INSTALLATION – The wood stove in this house will likely cause problems. Note that the chimney top is lower than the ceiling of the second storey – meaning that the house is a more effective stack than the chimney. Fires will be difficult to light because the system will produce a weak draft until the chimney is thoroughly warmed. Smoke may spill from the stove door when it is opened for loading wood. And there will be some risk of smoke spillage as the fire dies down to a coal bed.

You could improve this installation by moving the appliance and chimney to the wall that is next to the two-storey section of the house. The chimney would run inside the house and be protected from the cold. You could also make it tall enough to clear the roof of the taller section of the house (without it being unsightly). However, it might lose a lot of heat if it is too exposed, resulting in flue gas condensation, perhaps creosote deposits, along with a poor draft.

You can expect chimney draft and smoking problems if the wood-burning stove or fireplace in the basement is installed with an outside chimney. Avoid this form of installation, if possible.

Chimneys that run up through the house and exit at or near the roof peak can overcome the stack effect because they always produce a stronger draft than the house's stack effect. Stack effect is always present in houses, but you can minimize its influence by installing the chimney inside the house and placing it where it can penetrate the roof near the peak.

The Cold-Backdraft-at-Standby Syndrome

If you heat with wood, you may have experienced this situation: You go to the basement to build a fire in the wood stove. When you open the door to put in the newspaper and kindling, you are greeted by a blast of cold air. Then you light the kindling and the smoke comes into the room instead of going up the chimney.

This is the "cold-backdraft-at-standby" syndrome. Negative pressure in the house produced by operating a powerful fan like a kitchen exhaust fan can cause this reverse flow. Most often, it comes from the combined effect of an outside chimney and a basement location for an appliance.

Here's how it works. When there is no fire in the appliance, the air in the chimney cools to the outside temperature. The chimney produces no draft whatsoever. The slight negative pressure in the basement, caused by the house's stack effect, is enough to pull the cold air down the chimney and out through any openings in the stove.

Homeowners with installations that are susceptible to the syndrome have found ways to get the fire started. For example, they open a window on the same level, on the windward side of the house to relieve the negative pressure. Then they light some newspaper in the base of the chimney to get enough heat into the flue to produce some draft. But this and other techniques only mask the problem; they don't correct it.

To ensure that you never experience the cold-backdraft-at-standby syndrome, don't combine an outside chimney with a basement stove. Instead, install the stove on the main floor where you spend most of your waking hours, and use an inside chimney.

Maintaining your wood-burning system ranges from simple, frequent tasks such as removing and disposing of ashes to more complicated jobs such as replacing parts that have worn from usage and heat stress. Regular upkeep also helps the system operate efficiently and safely, since one of the most important maintenance tasks is removing combustible deposits from the flue pipe and chimney.

Wood-burning systems operate under a variety of conditions during each heating season, which creates the need for many maintenance tasks. In the spring and fall, heat demand is relatively low. So slow burning may cause creosote to build up in the flue pipe and chimney more rapidly. This is a common problem with conventional wood-burning stoves that can't burn at low heat outputs without smouldering.

During the colder months, wood-burning systems operate closer to their maximum heat output for long periods, creating stress on internal components. Many modern wood heaters have internal components, including baffles and catalytic combustors, that wear out from exposure to high temperatures. Replace these components when necessary.

One of the best ways to ensure that your wood-heating system is safe, clean and effective is to hire a trained, insured and certified chimney sweep to conduct a thorough maintenance check each year. Professional chimney sweeps will clean the entire system and report any problems. They might suggest that it is time to replace the flue pipes, baffles, catalytic combustor (if you have one) or door gaskets – and may even be able to do the work for you when the time comes. Your wood-heating retailer may also offer sweeping and maintenance services.

Summer is a good time to schedule maintenance, before you light the first autumn fire. It can also be done in the spring, following the winter wood-heating season.

Important Maintenance Tasks

Here are the most important maintenance tasks to consider as you look over your wood-heating system.

Clean and Inspect the Chimney and Flue Pipes

Check the chimney and flue pipes regularly until you determine the rate of creosote buildup. Chimney fires usually occur because users don't know how quickly the deposits develop and neglect to clean them. Check often and clean off the creosote when it is visible and clinging to the liner surface. Dry, flaky deposits are less dangerous than black, shiny creosote. Older or smouldering systems may need cleaning as often as every three weeks.

During a maintenance inspection, check the chimney and flue pipes for signs of deterioration. Check the flue pipes for corrosion that can weaken the joints. Look for corrosion or rust stains on the outer shell of a metal chimney, and check for bulges or corrosion in its inner liner.

When inspecting a masonry chimney, look for black or white stains on the outer bricks and cracks. Look for missing pieces in the chimney liner as well. Locate the clean-out door for the chimney – it is usually in the basement, below the point where the flue pipe enters the chimney (however, in some installations, it is outside the house). Open the clean-out door at the base of the chimney and check for tile fragments and liquid stains. Remove any deposits. Make sure the door is tightly sealed afterwards.

Check the condition of the chimney in hidden spaces – including the attic, wall and chimney chase areas – where corrosion and other deterioration can occur. Do the most thorough cleaning and inspection of the system in the spring, just after the heating season is over. Any deposits left in the system, combined with warm, humid summer air, may corrode the steel parts. Cleaning and inspecting the system in the spring also gives you time to order replacement parts and do any repairs before the heating season begins in the fall. If you see any problems during your cleaning and inspection and aren't sure how to handle them, have a qualified technician inspect and repair the system before you use it again.

Adjust Door Tension

Many modern wood heaters have adjustment screws on their loading doors. They are designed to keep tension on the door gasket to prevent smoke leakage. These adjustments are usually simple and keep the heater working. Adjust the door, for example, when you see a haze of soot on part of the door glass. You will be able to tell where the leak is from the shape of these streaks of haze.

Replace Door Gaskets and Other Seals

Appliance designers use gaskets to prevent unwanted air from entering the firebox. Leaky gaskets reduce efficiency and may disable the combustion system of an advanced wood burner. Gaskets are located around the loading door, the glass panel and most ash-pan openings. You may need to replace some gaskets as often as once a year; others may be fine after several years of use. Check all gaskets at least once a year during a thorough maintenance inspection and occasionally during the heating season.

Check and Replace Catalytic Combustors

If you have a catalytic stove, you can test the catalytic element's function by watching the smoke as it exits the chimney top. With a well-established fire burning, open the bypass damper and observe the top of the chimney – you will likely see some smoke. Then close the bypass damper, wait 10 minutes and check the chimney top again. If you still see smoke, remove the catalytic element and check it.

Examine the catalytic combustor and its mount during your maintenance checks. The combustor is fragile, so use a clean, soft paintbrush to remove ash dust. You may see cracks in the honeycomb of the catalyst, but they will not necessarily affect operation. If pieces are missing, replace the catalyst. A leaking bypass damper seal can dramatically increase emissions from a catalytic stove. Therefore, make sure you check the bypass gasket.

The catalyst in a high-efficiency wood stove is certified by the EPA or CSA B415.1 and is usually guaranteed for up to six years. Under heavy use, however, it may last only one to two years. If in doubt about when to replace these parts, ask your hearth products retailer.

Examine Baffle Plates

Components inside the combustion area of advanced wood-burning stoves and fireplaces are exposed to extremely high temperatures and may deteriorate with use. Internal baffles may last as long as 10 years or as little as two, depending on the design and on how you use the appliance.

Internal air channels and tubes may become disconnected or even fall into the firebox. Correct any such change to your stove immediately because performance will suffer and other internal components will likely be damaged.

Maintain Door Glass

The glass door in a modern wood-burner isn't glass at all, but a transparent ceramic material that can withstand very high temperatures. It is unlikely that the "glass" will break because of heat, but it could be damaged if struck with a hard object. If you need replacement glass, visit the store where you bought your stove or fireplace to get the right size, shape and material.

The door glass will need cleaning periodically – wait until the appliance has cooled before cleaning. A damp cloth or paper towel should remove any ash dust or light brown stains. For darker, more stubborn stains, buy special stove glass cleaner that will not scratch the surface. Check the special gasket around the glass and replace it when it gets worn or leaky.

Many of the new, high-efficiency stoves feature a forced-air mechanism that helps to keep the door glass clean.

12 Burning Wood Efficiently

By firing your wood-burning system correctly, you improve efficiency and reduce air pollution.

Owners must learn and practise the skills needed to operate their wood-burning system effectively. By mastering the techniques offered here, you will

- reduce the amount of wood you need to burn to heat your home;

- reduce outdoor and indoor air pollution from wood smoke;

- reduce the frequency of chimney cleaning; and

- increase the convenience and pleasure of wood burning.

The Basics: What Happens When Wood Burns

As firewood burns, it goes through three phases.

Boiling off the water – Up to half the weight of a freshly cut log is water. After proper seasoning, the water content is reduced to about 20 percent. As the wood is heated in the firebox, this water boils off, consuming heat energy in the process. The wetter the wood, the more heat energy is used to boil the water. That is why wet firewood hisses and sizzles and is hard to burn, while seasoned wood ignites and burns easily.

The emission of smoke – As the wood heats up and passes the boiling point of water, it starts to smoke. The smoke is the visible result of the solid wood decomposing as it vaporizes into a cloud of combustible gases and tars. If the temperature is high enough and oxygen is present, the smoke will burn. When it does, it produces the bright flames that are characteristic of wood combustion. If the smoke doesn't burn in the firebox, it exits the appliance into the flue pipe and chimney. Here it either condenses – forming creosote deposits – or is expelled as air pollution. Unburned smoke also represents a less efficient appliance because smoke contains much of the wood's total energy. Advanced combustion systems are designed to burn the smoke before it leaves the stove, which is one reason they are more efficient than older models.

The charcoal phase – After the water has boiled off and most of the gases and tars have vaporized out of the wood, charcoal remains. Charcoal is almost 100-percent carbon. It burns with a red glow and some flame or smoke when enough oxygen is present. Charcoal is a good fuel that burns easily. However, burning charcoal often produces carbon monoxide, a serious indoor air pollutant.

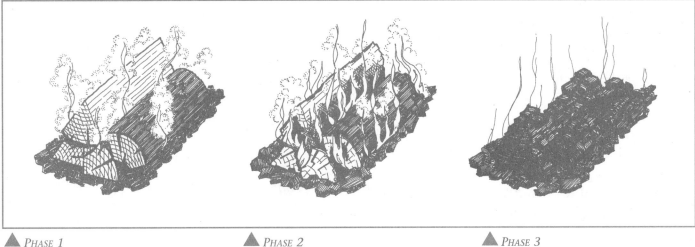

▲ *PHASE 1*
Evaporation of water

▲ *PHASE 2*
Emission of smoke

▲ *PHASE 3*
Charcoal

In practice, all three phases of wood combustion usually occur at the same time. The wood gases can flame and the edges of the pieces can glow red as charcoal burns, while water in the core of the piece is still evaporating. The challenge in burning wood effectively is to boil off the water in the wood quickly, while making sure the smoke burns with bright flames before it leaves the firebox.

With the new, advanced combustion designs, two flame zones are often visible: the primary flame that rises from the wood and the transparent secondary flame that swirls above the wood. Once a good fire is established and you turn down the air control, you can see the primary flames slow down and become smaller. To get a clean, efficient burn, make sure that there is always a secondary flame. A welcome feature of these advanced wood-burning designs is that the better the combustion and the cleaner the burn, the more interesting the flame looks.

Starting a Fire

You need the following ingredients to build and maintain a good wood fire:

- a properly designed and installed wood-burning system;

- newspapers (do not use coloured or coated paper);

- dry, finely split kindling in a variety of sizes; and

- dry cord firewood split into a range of sizes.

▲ *To Build a Kindling Fire – Use plenty of crumpled newspaper and dry, finely split kindling. Never use glossy paper or coloured advertising flyers. Open the air control fully. Light the newspaper near where the combustion air enters the firebox. When a kindling fire is built properly, you should expect rapid ignition with no smouldering. Never use liquids to start a fire.*

The first step in building a fire is to find out where the combustion air enters the firebox. In most advanced stoves and fireplaces, some air enters the firebox through a narrow strip above and behind the glass panel. This air wash flows down across the glass to the front of the fire. (It flows downward because it is cooler and heavier than the combustion gases.) Most models also have the primary air inlet near the bottom front of the firebox, usually just inside and below the loading door. This is where you light the fire, so that it gets plenty of air.

Next, crumple four or five sheets of newspaper and put them in the firebox. You may need more newspaper if your firebox is large or your kindling isn't dry or finely split. Many people make the mistake of using too little newspaper – be generous and you will have more success.

Hold the paper down with 10 to 15 pieces of dry kindling. Softwoods, such as cedar and pine, make good kindling (of course, use the species available in your region). Place the kindling on and behind the newspaper, so that the combustion air reaches the newspaper first where you light it. It is also a good idea to add one or two small pieces of dry firewood to the kindling load before lighting.

Open the air control fully, light the newspaper and close (but don't latch) the door. When the paper is flaming brightly and the kindling catches, latch the door. Some appliances have more restrictive air supplies than others, so you may have to leave the door ajar for as long as 15 minutes – until there is a hot kindling fire and the chimney is producing strong draft. Since leaving the door unlatched or open even slightly for extended periods may cause dangerously high temperatures, **NEVER** leave the stove unattended in this condition.

When starting a wood fire, your goal is to light it once and make sure the fuel ignites rapidly. Practise this procedure a few times – you might be surprised at how quickly you can establish a hot, bright fire. When the flames from the kindling load begin to subside, gradually add several small pieces of wood. Avoid smothering the fire with the new wood. Place the pieces on and behind the burning kindling.

Note

The suggestions offered here are general and apply to many wood-burning appliances. However, some combustion designs – notably some of the new advanced combustion stoves, catalytic systems and masonry heaters – may require special firing techniques. In this case, you should follow any detailed firing instructions in the operator's manual that came with your stove or fireplace.

An Alternative – Building a Top-Down Fire

You may find it convenient to build a wood fire using the top-down method. To build a top-down fire, reverse the procedure described in the "Starting a Fire" section above – that is, place two or three firewood pieces at the back of the firebox and lean 10 to 15 pieces of kindling against the logs. Then place several crumpled sheets of newspaper on and around the kindling. Open the air control fully, light the news-paper and close the loading door. The fire will start reliably and progress to the large pieces of wood without any further poking or adjustment.

There are several advantages to the top-down fire building method:

- there is less visible start-up smoke at the top of the chimney;
- there is little chance that the fire will collapse and smother itself; and
- you do not need to open the loading door to add larger pieces once you establish the kindling fire.

The top-down fire technique isn't appropriate for every type of wood-burning appliance, but it can be effective in some cases.

Rekindling a Fire from Charcoal

In many wood-burning stoves and fireplaces, there will be live coals toward the back of the firebox, furthest from the air supply, after the fire has burned down. To rekindle them, first remove the ashes from the front of the firebox, then rake the live coals forward until they are just inside the loading door. If only a small amount of charcoal remains, you will have to start with kindling. If you have a good quantity of glowing charcoal to work with, place the new load of firewood on and behind the charcoal. Open the air inlets fully and close the door.

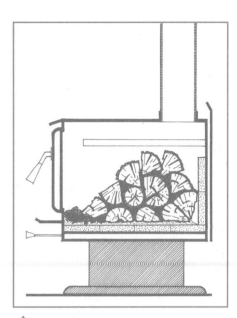

▲ *To Rekindle a Fire from Hot Coals – Rake the charcoal toward the front of the stove where the combustion air enters. Place the pieces of wood on and behind the coals. Open the air inlet fully and leave it open until the wood pieces are well charred. This illustration shows how pieces are arranged for an extended fire.*

With some of the new, high-efficiency combustion stoves, you have to alter the procedure slightly. Read the manufacturer's instructions and experiment a little. For example, some designs require you to make a channel through the ash pit from front to back, underneath the wood.

Once you have added new wood to the charcoal, expect it to ignite almost instantly. The bottom pieces may even start flaming before you get the door closed. Allow the fire to burn with bright, turbulent flames until the wood is charred. This usually takes between 10 and 20 minutes, depending on the size of the pieces and the moisture content of the wood.

When the wood is charred, gradually reduce the air setting to produce the amount of heat and length of burn you desire. You may want to try reducing the air control setting in two or three stages. The result will be less smoke because the fire won't have to recover from a single, large reduction in air supply.

Remember the most important rule: **Never let the fire smoulder.** As long as there is solid wood in the firebox, there should be active flames. Without flames, smoke will escape unburned, reducing efficiency and increasing pollution. With advanced systems, you can achieve a reliable overnight burn while maintaining flaming combustion and still have enough charcoal in the morning to kindle a new fire.

Other Useful Tips

Arranging the Firewood – Small pieces of firewood arranged loosely in a crisscross pattern burn quickly because the combustion air can reach all of the pieces at once. Larger pieces in a compact pile burn more slowly because there are fewer spaces for the air to penetrate the load. Try to add more than one piece of wood to a fire – you need three or more pieces to form a sheltered pocket of glowing coals that reflect heat toward each other and sustain the fire.

Firing in Cycles – Don't expect the fire to provide perfectly steady heat output. A wood fire burns best in cycles. A **cycle** starts when a new load of wood ignites from a charcoal bed and ends when that load is consumed and becomes another bed. Each cycle provides three to eight hours of heating, depending on how much wood you use, how much heat you need and how large your firebox is. Plan the firing cycles around your household routine. Be cautious about leaving the stove unattended when you are away.

Using a Flash Fire – A flash fire is a small amount of wood burned quickly. Use it in spring and fall when you just want to take the chill off the house. The flash fire technique eliminates the smouldering fires that are common in the spring and fall. To build a flash fire, rake the charcoal toward the air inlets and place several small pieces of

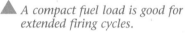

▲ *A small, loosely stacked fuel load is good for short-duration flash fires.*

▲ *A compact fuel load is good for extended firing cycles.*

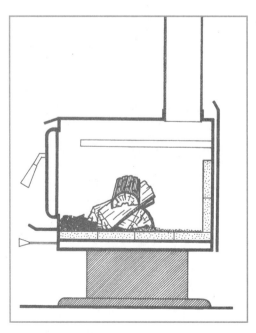

◄ *LOADING FOR A FLASH FIRE – Use a few small pieces of wood for short fires to "take the chill off." Load the wood loosely in a crisscross arrangement. Let the fire burn brightly until most of the solid wood is burned, then reduce the air setting. Flash fires are effective in spring and fall when the heating load is modest. By using the flash fire technique, you avoid smouldering fires.*

wood on and behind it. Stack the pieces loosely in a crisscross arrangement. Open the air inlet to produce a hot, bright fire. You may reduce the air supply slightly as the fire progresses, but never enough to extinguish the flames.

Extending a Fire – To achieve a longer-lasting fire – to heat the house overnight or while you are away – rake the coals toward the air inlet and use larger pieces of wood placed compactly in the firebox. Placing the pieces close together prevents the heat and flame from penetrating the load and saves the buried pieces for later in the burn cycle. Open the air inlets fully for five to 20 minutes, depending on load size and fuel moisture content. When the outer pieces have a thick layer of charcoal, reduce the air control in stages to the desired level.

Removing Ashes – Some advanced combustion stoves have ash pans as standard equipment or as an option. Some use a simple grate through which ashes drop into the pan. Others have a plug in the stove floor that, when lifted, allows ashes to fall into the pan. Make sure that the ash door is well closed and sealed. If your stove doesn't have an ash pan, ask your local retailer for an ash handler into which you can scoop ashes through the loading door.

The ashes may contain live coals that can stay hot for days. If you don't dispose of them carefully, they can pose a fire hazard. Place ashes in their own metal container and keep that container on a non-combustible floor, preferably outside the house. Special double-bottom ash containers – with tight-fitting lids designed to hold ashes until they are cool – are available in stove and fireplace stores.

There are many ways to use or dispose of wood ashes. Some people use ashes for traction on driveway ice, to control garden pests or to reduce soil acidity. Other people simply bury them. Rural municipal waste disposal sites usually have special areas for ashes. Consider disposing of your wood ashes in a safe, clean and environmentally friendly way.

Using a Thermometer – A thermometer helps you use your wood burner more effectively, particularly if you can't view the fire through glass doors. There are two types of thermometers. One has a *probe* that you put into the flue gas stream through a small hole in the flue pipe. The second is a *magnetic* thermometer that sticks to the outside of the flue pipe or stove top.

Install the probe-type thermometer in the flue pipe about 50 cm (20 in.) downstream from the exit of the appliance – but never on the appliance. The stack thermometer tells you how hot the flue gases are.

The magnetic thermometer, on the other hand, measures the temperature of the flue pipe, so its temperature will be lower than the probe thermometer's.

Some manufacturers recommend the use of a stove-top thermometer, rather than a stack thermometer. It works the same way, but the temperature range will be different since it measures the surface temperature of the stove.

When you fire the stove at a high temperature to drive moisture out of the fuel, use a thermometer to tell you when you can reduce the air supply. Every wood-heating system behaves differently and thermometers vary, so there are no exact temperatures that you can follow. However, to avoid damaging the stove's internal parts, don't let the flue gas temperature rise above 460°C (860°F) on a stack temperature probe for more than a few minutes. Learn which burning connections result in the stack temperature you measure. With experience, you will be able to tell by the thermometer if you have set the air control too low and when you should reload.

Advanced combustion wood stoves do not need thermometers as much as older equipment does. You can check the condition of the fire visually. If the fire is burning properly, the glass door stays clear. If the glass becomes hazy or develops dark stains quickly, the fire has been turned down too low or the firewood is too wet. The glass should stay clear when the fire has a higher heat output and the firewood is of good quality. Another indicator is the flame itself. The more complex the flame, the better the combustion in the stove.

The Efficient Wood Fire in an Advanced Stove

When you master the techniques for efficient wood burning, here is what you should see.

- When wood burns, it flames until only charcoal remains. (If there are no flames, something is wrong.)

- If there are firebricks in the firebox, they will be tan, never black.

- Steel or cast-iron parts in the firebox will be light to dark brown, never black or shiny.

- If the wood is seasoned and well split, the air settings are correct and the load is arranged properly, a new load of wood will ignite rapidly from the charcoal – some pieces will be flaming before the door is closed. If the appliance has a glass door with an air wash, it will be clear. If the appliance has a glass door without an air wash, it will be hazy, but it should never be black.

- The exhaust from the top of the chimney will be clear or, in winter, white with steam. A plume of blue or grey smoke indicates smouldering and poor combustion.

The efficiency and convenience of your wood-heating system depend significantly on the quality of the fuel wood you burn. The four main factors that influence how firewood burns are moisture content, piece size, wood condition and tree species.

The **moisture content** of the wood affects the rate at which it burns and the efficiency of combustion. When trees are cut, the wood moisture content can range between 35 and 60 percent by weight. Wood that is this wet is hard to ignite and slow to burn. It also hisses and sizzles in the firebox. It combusts poorly and produces large amounts of air pollutants. Energy from the burning fire is used to boil off the moisture, which reduces efficiency. Wet wood is the most common problem with wood heating. If you think you have a problem with your stove's performance, check the dryness of your fuel first. Properly seasoned wood ignites readily, flames easily and burns efficiently.

Cut and split firewood in the early spring. Stack your wood outside. It dries best if you keep it off the ground and covered. Allow room for the air to flow under the stack and to circulate between the pieces. During the summer, as warm breezes flow through the stacks and carry away the water, the moisture content of the wood falls to about 20 percent. One sign of

Burning wet wood produces more smoke than heat. Dried, well-seasoned wood will smoke less and give you more heat. One way to verify if a chunk of wood is dry is to look for checks and cracks at the ends. A cord that has been stacked to dry over one heating season should also be dry enough to burn. However, if you aren't sure, you can test the wood with a moisture meter. To use it, merely jab the prongs into a chunk of wood to get a reading. Ideally, the reading will be between 18 and 22. You can get a moisture meter at some hardware stores for between $35 and $60. You will also find them at your hearth products retailer. High-end models, such as those used in laboratories, are available for around $240.

dry wood is checks or cracks in the ends of the pieces. Properly dried firewood is darker on the ends than freshly cut wood and weighs much less.

The **size of the firewood pieces** affects the rate of combustion. Large pieces ignite and release their energy more slowly than small pieces. Smaller, more finely split pieces are better for short,

hot fires, while larger pieces suit extended firing cycles. In general, the firewood produced by commercial dealers comes in pieces that are larger across than modern wood-burners need. You may need to split some of the wood again before using it. The largest piece of wood for the new, advanced stoves should be no more than about 15 cm (6 in.) across. You also need a range of smaller pieces for effective stoking.

Another factor that affects how firewood burns is the **wood's condition**. Wood that has been lying in a swampy area or has been cut too long ago (more than three years) will be difficult to burn. It tends to look or feel rotten.

Remember, storing wet wood indoors could create mould inside the house, so you should limit the amount of wood that you store inside.

Store two or three days' supply of wood indoors, making sure that it is clean and dry. In winter, when you bring wood directly in from the cold outdoors and immediately load it into the appliance, it may initially cool the fire and prevent proper combustion.

▲ *Look for checks and cracks at the ends.*

Several **tree species** are used for firewood, and those you choose will affect your wood-burning system. Below is a list of the tree species commonly used for firewood, according to their relative densities. Trees at the top of the list have the hardest wood and the most energy per cord, while those toward the bottom of the list are the softest and have the least energy per cord. Regardless of where you live and what species are available, try to mix the load as much as possible. This will ensure that you do not use too much wood of one species as your primary fuel source.

The energy content of wood per dry kilogram (i.e., per unit of weight) is similar regardless of species. However, the energy output from each piece of wood (weight per unit volume) of various species differs widely. Wood is generally sold by volume (cords), which means the energy per cord can differ widely among different species of wood. In general, hardwoods like maple, oak and beech are denser and have more energy per piece than softwoods such as pine, spruce and cedar. Softwoods and hardwoods tend to burn differently due to differences in density and resin content.

In most cases, when and where it is available, hardwood is the preferred firewood because it tends to produce a longer-lasting burn. Softwood can also be used successfully for fires, even in some of the coldest areas of the country. Softwoods are also by far the most common trees on Canada's coasts and northern areas. If you use softwood, you may need a wood stove with a larger firebox to handle the larger volume needed for the same amount of heating power. Even in areas where hardwoods are plentiful, softwood is a good fuel in the spring and fall when the heat demand is lower. The new high-efficiency stoves and fireplace designs burn both hardwood and softwood equally well.

Buying Firewood

Try to buy your wood from someone who uses good forest management practices. Environmentally sound woodlot management involves thinning out dying and damaged trees and less desirable species. To support sustainable forestry practices, use wood from a blend of species; burn the softer woods – such as pine, poplar and aspen – in the spring and fall. This way, you help ensure that wood remains a renewable energy source for home heating.

Try to mix your wood species as much as possible so that you use hardwoods and softwoods when they are available. Using a mix of species helps maintain the forest's natural diversity.

How is firewood measured for sale? As stated in Measurement Canada's official brochure Buying Firewood? Don't Get Burned!, most firewood in Canada is sold by the cord.

How do you know when a cord is a cord? A cord is a legal unit of measurement defined by the Weights and Measures Regulations as 3.62 m³ (128 cubic feet) of stacked roundwood (whole or split, with or without bark) containing wood and airspace with all bolts of similar length piled in a regular manner with their longitudinal axes approximately parallel.

Density of Common Firewoods

Here is a list of the tree species commonly used for firewood. Those at the top of the list are hardest and those toward the bottom of the list are the softest.

HARD

Ironwood
Rock elm
Hickory
Oak
Sugar maple
Beech
Yellow birch
Ash
Red elm
Red maple
Tamarack
Douglas fir
White birch
Manitoba maple
Red alder
Hemlock
Poplar
Pine
Basswood
Spruce
Balsam

SOFT

Firewood Cords

Firewood is measured and sold in units called cords. A **full cord** measures 1.2 × 2.4 × 1.2 m (4 × 8 × 4 ft.) and is the official firewood measure. However, long lengths, such as 1.2 m (4 ft.), are usually cut into smaller pieces for home heating. Other terms – such as **face cord**, **stove cord** or **furnace cord** – are used to describe a stack of wood measuring 1.2 × 2.4 m (4 × 8 ft.), with the length of the pieces shorter than 1.2 m (4 ft.). Firewood is most often sold in face or stove cords made up of pieces 30 or 40 cm (12 or 16 in.) long.

These various cord measures can be confusing. If you want to compare prices from several suppliers, take a tape measure to each dealer's yard and measure a few pieces to determine an average length. If the dealer doesn't price the wood in the standard full-cord measure, convert the price to this basic unit.

Three examples are provided on page 52 to illustrate the conversion.

If possible, avoid buying firewood in units that can't be converted to the standard full cord. For example, truckloads of wood are difficult to measure so you could be overcharged without knowing it. Measurement Canada's brochure *Buying Firewood? Don't Get Burned!* highlights some precautions you can take when you receive your wood, to ensure that you are getting the amount you paid for.

Tips for Buying Wood

When ordering firewood

When ordering your wood, ask the dealer what kind of wood it is and how the cords are measured so that you aren't surprised when the truck arrives. Also, ask for the wood to be delivered stacked in the truck, so you can measure it before it is unloaded. If this isn't possible, stack the firewood immediately following delivery. Measure the length, width and height of the stack, and calculate the quantity that you received.

When receiving the firewood

Be present when the wood is delivered. Don't rely on a neighbour to accept delivery on your behalf. When the wood arrives, take the time to randomly examine some pieces in front of

---

What to burn?

ALWAYS BURN

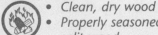
- *Clean, dry wood*
- *Properly seasoned, split wood*
- *A mix of hard and soft wood, where possible, depending on what is available in your region*

NEVER BURN

- *Wet or green wood*
- *Household garbage such as plastic or cardboard*
- *Painted or stained wood*
- *Pressure-treated wood*
- *Particleboard or plywood*
- *Ocean driftwood*
- *Glossy magazines*
- *Any materials prohibited by local by-laws*

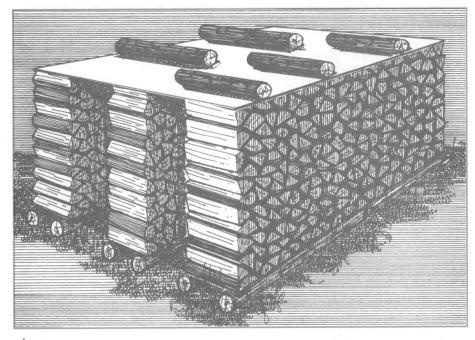

▲ THE FIREWOOD CORD – *Firewood is measured in cords. A **full** cord measures 1.2 m × 2.4 m × 1.2 m (4 ft. × 8 ft. × 4 ft.). Many firewood dealers sell partial cords called face or stove cords. Pictured are three face cords with pieces measuring an average of 40 cm (16 in.). Together, these three face cords make up one full cord and should equal 3.6 m³ (128 cubic feet).*

Example 1

*Woody Cutters sells a **face cord** for $55. You find that the pile is 1.2 m (4 ft.) high and 2.4 m (8 ft.) long, with an average length of 40 cm (16 in.). To find the price for a full cord, divide the imperial length of the logs (16 in.) into the full cord length (48 in.), then multiply it by the price, as follows:*

(48 [**full cord** length]
÷ 16 [average chunk length])
× $55 (price of **face cord**)

= $165 (price of **full cord**).

Therefore, Woody Cutters sells firewood for $165 per full cord.

Example 3

*The Cut Above Woodlot sells a 1.2 m × 2.4 m × 45 cm (4 ft. × 8 ft. × 18 in.) **furnace cord** for $75. To determine the price for a full cord, the calculation is as follows:*

(48 [**full cord** length]
÷ 18 [chunk length])
× $75 (price of **furnace cord**)

= $200 (price of **full cord**).

Therefore, the Cut Above Woodlot sells firewood for $200 per full cord.

Example 2

*The Charlebois Sugar Bush sells a **stove cord** for $45. The pile measures 1.2 m (4 ft.) by 2.4 m (8 ft.), with an average length of 30 cm (12 in.). To determine the price for a full cord, the following calculation is used:*

(48 [**full cord** length]
÷ 12 [average chunk length])
× $45 (price of **stove cord**)

= $180 (price of **full cord**).

Therefore, the Charlebois Sugar Bush sells firewood for $180 per full cord.

Know your wood, and make sure it is dry if you've paid for seasoned wood

Although you may not be an expert on various tree species, make an effort to learn about the species in your area. Therefore, if you are expecting to receive a certain species, you can identify it. Moreover, if you are paying a premium to make sure the wood has already been seasoned, look for checks and cracks at the end of pieces or jab a few pieces with your moisture meter.

Before using any firewood

Verify that the quantity received is the same as the quantity that you paid for. If there is a difference, contact the seller before you use any of the firewood. If the quality of the wood is questionable – if it is rotten, mouldy or soaking wet – you aren't getting your money's worth.

Buying Firewood? Don't Get Burned! is available on-line at http://www.nrcan.gc.ca/es/erb/reed/public_e.htm.

Where to Get Firewood

You can usually find firewood dealers listed in the Yellow Pages of the telephone directory or in the classified ads of your local newspaper. Better yet, get a referral from neighbours who purchase firewood.

You may be able to get a fuel wood permit to cut the trees yourself from the local office of your provincial or territorial natural resources ministry. Sawmills may also have cut-offs, slabs and cull logs that they sell as firewood. You will still have to cut the wood into pieces, so that they fit into your stove properly. If you fill the stove with too much wood without leaving enough space around the pieces for good air and fire circulation, you won't get an efficient fire.

One way to save money is to buy logs from a local woodlot. Seek out one that is known to practise sustainable forest management. Unprocessed logs usually measure 1.2 to 2.4 metres (four to eight feet) in length. You will need a chainsaw to cut the logs to length and a splitting ax or maul to split the wood into the right size of pieces.

the delivery person to make sure the load isn't rotten. Then make sure that you get a receipt which shows the quantity and type of firewood purchased; the seller's name, address and telephone number; and the price paid.

How Much is Enough?

Only experience can tell you how much wood you will need for a heating season. A medium-sized modern home, if heated exclusively with wood, requires between three and five full cords per winter – or more if the house isn't energy efficient. On the other hand, the same house with a high-efficiency combustion wood stove that is properly located in the main living area might use only one or two full cords. You need more wood if your area is very cold; if your house is large, leaky or poorly insulated; or if you only use softwoods.

Properly stored firewood will last for more than one year, so buy a little extra if you can find good quality wood at a reasonable price and if you have a place to store it outdoors.

Remember, storing wet wood indoors could create mould inside the house, so you should limit the amount of wood that you store inside.

Are wood pellets your fuel source?

Buying wood pellets

You can purchase bags of wood pellets in the seasonal section of large home improvement stores or at local hardware stores. You can often buy wood pellets through agricultural co-ops. The bags come in several sizes; the most common is 18.1 kilograms (40 pounds), which may cost between $4 and $6. You can have bulk orders delivered on a wooden pallet for a delivery charge. Ask your dealer where the pellets were stored over the winter. If they were stored outdoors, make sure that the pellets that you purchase are dry, or else you will be paying for mushy sawdust which you can't use in your stove.

If your pellet stove is your home's primary or secondary heating source, make sure that you have enough bags on hand before the heating season begins.

Storing wood pellets

Wood pellets are simply compressed pellets of sawdust, so you must store them in a dry area, where they will not take on moisture or bugs. You can store bags of wood pellets in the basement or an attached garage, but they should be kept off the ground, preferably on the pallet on which they are delivered. Stack them so that the pile won't topple over when you reach for a bag. Pick a spot to pile your bags and leave them there. Excessive handling of the bags could cause the pellet coating to crack, leaving you with miniature handfuls of sawdust.

Buying and storing pellets made of corn and corn kernels

Some stoves are fuelled by corn pellets or corn kernels, which may be more difficult to find. Corn-burning stoves have not been rated for energy efficiency or smoke emissions, and some insurance companies will not insure them. If you use a corn stove, you still must keep the fuel dry. Corn pellets and kernels may be available through an agricultural co-op.

Reuse and recycle your pellet bags

The pellets come in poly bags that can be easily reused and, in some cases, recycled. Your municipality can confirm which disposal method is the most environmentally friendly for your area.

You may want to calculate the cost of using wood fuel compared with conventional fuels such as oil, natural gas, propane or electricity. The procedure outlined here can provide reasonably accurate comparative costs. You will first need to find out the cost of the fuels in your area that you want to compare.

Step 1. Determine the Price of Energy Sources in Your Area

Call your local suppliers to find out the average cost of the energy sources you are comparing. The cost should be the total cost as delivered to your home. Be sure to get the prices in the same units for the energy sources, as shown in Table 1.

Note that the figures for firewood are for full cords (1.2 × 2.4 × 1.2 m, or 4 × 8 × 4 ft.). Often, you will be quoted the price for a face or stove cord, or one third of a full cord. If so, multiply by three to get the price for a full cord. The energy content figures are in metric units called megajoules (MJ).

Table 1: Energy Content and Local Price of Various Fuels

Fuel	Energy Content	Your Local Price
Oil	38.2 MJ/litre	_____/litre
Electricity	3.6 MJ/kWh	_____/kWh
Natural Gas	37.5 MJ/m³	_____/m³
Propane	25.3 MJ/litre	_____/litre
Hardwood (air dried)	30 600 MJ/cord	_____/cord
Softwood (air dried)	18 700 MJ/cord	_____/cord
Mixed Hardwood (air dried)	25 000 MJ/cord	_____/cord
Wood Pellets	19 800 MJ/tonne	_____/tonne

Step 2. Select the Type of Heating Systems You Wish to Compare

Choose the types of equipment you want to compare from the list of systems in Table 2. Seasonal efficiency figures for the equipment are in the right-hand column. Using these efficiency figures, you can calculate the savings you can achieve by upgrading an older system to a new, more efficient appliance and/or by changing to a different energy source.

Table 2: Typical Seasonal Heating System Efficiencies

Fuel	Type of System		% Efficiency
Oil	Conventional Burner		60
	Retention Head Burner		70–78
	Advanced Mid-Efficiency Furnace		83–89
Electricity	Central Furnace or Baseboard		95–100
Natural Gas	Central Furnace	– conventional	55–65
		– powered exhaust	75–82
		– condensing	88–96
Propane	Central Furnace	– conventional	55–65
		– powered exhaust	76–83
		– condensing	85–93
Wood	Central Furnace		45–55
	Conventional Stove (properly located)		55–70
	"High Tech" Stove (properly located)		70–80
Wood Pellets	Pellet Stove		55–80

Step 3. Choose Housing Type and Annual Heating Loads

From the list in Table 3, select the city and housing type that are closest to yours. The heating loads are in metric units called gigajoules (GJ).

Table 3: Typical Annual Heating Loads in Gigajoules (GJ) for Various Housing Types in Canadian Cities

City	Old Detached	New Detached	New Semi-Detached	New Townhouse
Victoria/Vancouver	85	60	45	30
Prince George	150	110	80	60
Calgary	120	90	65	50
Edmonton	130	95	70	55
Fort McMurray/ Prince Albert	140	105	80	60
Regina/Saskatoon/ Winnipeg	130	90	70	50
Whitehorse	155	115	85	60
Yellowknife	195	145	110	80
Thunder Bay	130	95	70	55
Sudbury	120	90	65	50
Ottawa	110	75	55	40
Toronto	95	65	45	35
Windsor	80	55	40	30
Montréal	110	80	60	45
Québec	115	85	65	50
Chicoutimi	125	90	70	55
Saint John	105	75	60	45
Edmundston	120	90	65	50
Charlottetown	110	80	60	45
Halifax	100	75	55	40
St. John's	120	85	60	45

Note: "New" means houses built after 1990, and "old" means houses built before 1990. Due to construction practices, weatherizing and re-insulating (which can be different from house to house), these figures are meant to be used only as general guidelines; they should not substitute for an accurate heating requirement determination, as discussed in Chapter 6.

Assumptions:
New townhouse – inside unit, approximately 93 m² (1000 sq. ft.)
New semi-detached – approximately 139 m² (1500 sq. ft.)
New detached – approximately 186 m² (2000 sq. ft.)
Old detached – approximately 186 m² (2000 sq. ft.)

Step 4. Using the Formula

Calculate the annual heating cost as follows:

$$\frac{\text{Energy cost/unit}}{\text{Energy content}} \times \frac{\text{Heat load}}{\text{System efficiency}} \times 100\ 000 = \text{Approximate annual heating cost}$$

Enter the cost per unit of energy and divide it by the energy content of the fuel (both figures come from Table 1). Select the annual heating load for your location and housing type from Table 3, and divide it by the efficiency of the proposed heating system from Table 2. Multiply the results of these two calculations, then multiply that result by 100 000.

When doing this calculation, verify the fuel costs in your area, as prices may vary. Also, the energy consumption of your particular house may be significantly different from the nominal houses in Table 3.

Sample Calculations

Example 1

The Burnett family has just built an open, detached home in Charlottetown, Prince Edward Island. They are thinking about buying a new, 83-percent efficient oil furnace. They want to determine whether it will be less expensive to heat the house with a high-efficiency advanced combustion wood stove at 70-percent efficiency than with their good oil furnace. Oil costs 45 cents a litre and mixed hardwood costs $160 per cord.

- from Table 3, for a new detached house in Charlottetown, annual heating load = 80 GJ

- from Table 1, energy content of oil = 38.2 MJ/L and energy content of wood = 25 000 MJ/cord

The annual cost of oil heating with a seasonal efficiency of 83 percent would be

$(0.45 \div 38.2) \times (80 \div 83) \times 100\ 000 = \$1{,}135.$

The annual cost of wood heating with a seasonal efficiency of 70 percent would be

$(160 \div 25\ 000) \times (80 \div 70) \times 100\ 000 = \$731.$

In this example, if wood displaced all of the oil previously used for heating, the Burnetts would save $404 per year ($1,135 – $731).

Example 2

The Laurin family lives in an old, detached, relatively open-plan house in Sudbury, Ontario. They presently heat their house with electric baseboards at a cost of eight cents per kilowatt hour (kWh). What would it cost them to heat with a high-efficiency advanced combustion wood stove with an efficiency of 70 percent? The cost of a full cord of hardwood is $150.

- from Table 3, annual heating load = 120 GJ

- from Table 1, energy content of electricity = 3.6 MJ/kWh and energy content of wood = 30 600 MJ/cord

- seasonal efficiency of electricity = 100 percent and seasonal efficiency of wood = 70 percent

The annual cost of electric heating would be

$(0.08 \div 3.6) \times (120 \div 100) \times 100\,000 = \$2,667$.

The annual cost of wood heating would be

$(150 \div 30\,600) \times (120 \div 70) \times 100\,000 = \$840$.

In this example, if the high-efficiency wood stove displaced all of the electricity previously used for heating, the Laurins would save $1,827 per year ($2,667 − $840).

Example 3

The Tran family lives in an old house in Prince George, British Columbia. They have an annual heating load of 150 GJ. They are trying to decide whether to heat the house with an efficient, direct-vent, freestanding propane fireplace at 72-percent efficiency or an advanced combustion wood fireplace at 70-percent efficiency. Propane costs 59 cents per litre and a full cord costs $110.

- from Table 1, the energy content of propane is 25.3 MJ/L

- the energy content of softwood is 18 700 MJ/cord

The annual cost of heating with propane would be

$(0.59 \div 25.3) \times (150 \div 72) \times 100\,000 = \$4,858$

The annual cost of heating with wood would be

$(110 \div 18\,700) \times (150 \div 70) \times 100\,000 = \$1,260$

Therefore, it would cost the Trans $3,598 ($4,858 − $1,260) less per year to heat their house with wood instead of propane, given the fuel prices chosen.

15 The Future of Residential Wood Heating

The demand for environmentally acceptable energy alternatives should ensure that wood heating will play an integral part of our energy mix for the foreseeable future. Many Canadians like you who use renewable energy sources to heat their homes want to make sure that these sources will remain sustainable. As well, they usually support model forest management practices. Moreover, with more highly efficient combustion technologies in homes – technologies that produce more heat with fewer pollutants – residential wood heating is expected to remain a safe, clean and efficient home-heating option in the future.

Wood stoves have evolved significantly since the late 1980s, and they are now cleaner-burning, easier to use and provide better environmental performance. As we understand more about efficient wood-burning techniques and the need to reduce smoke emissions, wood heating will be among the methods for improving Canada's energy security. More Canadian families will enjoy the benefits of advanced, certified clean-burning wood heaters.

Conventional fireplaces, once common in Canadian homes, are declining in popularity. Their low efficiency, high levels of pollution, limited use and often severe functional problems outweigh any claims to aesthetic appeal. In their place, energy-efficient and low-emission wood-burning fireplaces and inserts with their beautiful fire-viewing capabilities will become the accepted standard. These new fireplaces are as practical as they are attractive – something that can't be said of older, conventional fireplaces.

As the cost of heating homes with fossil fuels and electricity continues to rise, advanced wood burning offers an effective alternative. In the future, more Canadians – especially those living at the urban fringe and beyond – will return to Canada's original source of fuel. Installing an advanced technology wood stove, fireplace or insert in the primary living area may reduce the need to directly heat unoccupied parts of our homes. As we better understand the environmental and social costs of energy, the move to renewable, efficient and self-reliant wood will make more sense for many Canadians.

For More Information

Heating your home with wood requires a serious investment. For more information or tips on home heating with wood, consult the following wood-heating specialists:

Fuel Wood

- Provincial and territorial ministries of natural resources, energy or environment.
- Your local telephone directory, under "Firewood."
- Classified ads in your local newspaper.
- Word-of-mouth recommendations of owners who manage environmentally sound woodlots.

Products and Services

- Your local telephone directory, under "Chimneys," "Chimney Cleaning," "Heating Contractors," "Fireplaces and Wood Stoves – Retail."
- Visit your local hearth products store.
- Hearth Patio and Barbecue Association of Canada or Association des professionnels du chauffage.

Hearth Patio and Barbecue Association of Canada (HPBAC)

To find out more about hearth products or to locate qualified industry professionals, look for this logo in telephone directories.

Tel.: (705) 788-2221
E-mail: hpac@on.aibn.com

Association des professionnels du chauffage (APC)

C.P.170, succursale Beaubien
Montréal QC H2G 3C9
Tel.: (514) 270-4944
Fax: (514) 270-5488
E-mail: apc@poelesfoyers.ca

Contact the APC for fact sheets and other information on wood heating in Quebec.

CSA International

178 Rexdale Boulevard
Toronto, ON M9W 1R3

Contact CSA International for copies of standards mentioned in this guide.

Safety Information

- Your municipal office for building inspection and fire inspection
- Your provincial or territorial fire marshal's office

- Fire Prevention Canada (1 800 668-2955 or http://www.fiprecan.ca).

Wood Energy Technology Transfer Inc.

365 Bloor Street East
Suite 1807
Toronto ON M4W 3L4
Tel.: 1 888 358-9388
Web site: http://www.wettinc.ca

Consumer Tips

The Wood Heat Organization Inc.

410 Bank Street, Suite 117
Ottawa ON K2P 1Y8
Tel.: (613) 757-2290
Fax: (613) 757-0277
Web site:
http://www.woodheat.org

A comprehensive database on frequently asked questions is available on the Wood Heat Organization's Web site.

Publications on Residential Wood-Heating

A Guide to Residential Wood Heating is part of a series of buyer's guides for renewable energy systems for residential use. Other documents on residential wood heating include the following:

- *All About Wood Fireplaces*
- *An Introduction to Home Heating With Wood*
- *Buying a High-Efficiency Wood-Burning Appliance*
- *Getting the Most Out of Your Wood Stove*

Visit the Renewable and Electrical Energy Division (REED) Web site for these on-line publications or others at http://www.nrcan.gc.ca/redi.

Call 1 800 387-2000 toll-free to get your copies of these free guides.

For additional copies of *A Guide to Residential Wood Heating* or other publications on energy efficiency, write to

Energy Publications
DLS
Ottawa ON K1A 0S9
Tel.: 1 800 387-2000

In the National Capital Region, call 995-2943
Fax: (819) 994-1498

Canada Mortgage and Housing Corporation
Canadian Housing
  Information Centre
700 Montreal Road
Ottawa ON K1A 0P7
Tel.: (613) 748-2367
Fax: (613) 748-4069

For a copy of *Buying Firewood? Don't Get Burned!*, contact Measurement Canada, an Industry Canada agency, at http://strategis.ic.gc.ca/sc_mrksv/meascan/engdoc/homepage.html.

Call the **ministry of energy or natural resources in your province or territory.**

Notes:

Notes:

Notes:

Notes: